THE LOVE SEAT
Sherise Seven

Juan Derful, Ink
Los Angeles

Sherise Seven is an author and illustrator living in Los Angeles. Apparently she hates writing bios.

This book is dedicated to love. Actual love. So many today base their feelings on what they see rather than what they feel. Love has become a light feather that floats on the surface of life. A throw away feeling that can come and go. Love is deeper. Love rests on the bottom of the lake. Love doesn't happen in a day, week or month. Love is the ride of a lifetime. The ups and downs, the twists and turns. Love is the wind in your face as you sail across the ocean. My wish for you is that you experience *real* love in your lifetime.

Denise, December 12th

I hate my life. I hate my husband. I hate my house. I hate laundry. I hate making macaroni and cheese night after night, after night, after night. I hate picking up Disney Princess shoes from the same spot every freaking day. I hate starchy AM newscasters. I hate them because they see me every morning in a t-shirt with messy, oily hair. They are always so clean, crisp, laughing and talking about the world. They tell of horrific events in the world and then stuff croissants in their faces for the next story, laughing over nothing. They complain about getting up early to go to work and yet sit there sipping coffee in their pretty clothes. I get up early, in old stained clothing with holes in them. I talk about homework not done and waking up to dog throw up in my hair.

I hate the mailman. He brings the only excitement I get all day long. I hate soccer. I hate little league. I hate ballet. I hate gymnastics. I hate karate. I hate tennis. I hate homework. Tests. Spelling. Field trips. I hate the

PTA. I hate every other mom that I see at my kids' schools every day. It could be fake, but they always seem so happy. I don't buy that they're content and fulfilled inside just because they get weekly manicures and massages. I hate grocery shopping. It's really one of the most horrible events in my life. You are sitting at home, looking like a total disgusting slob and semi-homeless. The oil from your hair could be collected and used to fry a grilled cheese sandwich. Then it hits you, *we are out of milk.* Do you take the next hour to shower, shampoo and shine? Just to go get milk? OR, do you risk being seen and dash into the market to get the ONE freaking thing you need. Of course I always risk it, and that's the time you run into the hot dad in your kid's class.

I hate shopping for small human clothes. I hate taking the dogs to the vet. I hate feeding the dogs. A huge dread fills me when I see the dog water bowl and food bowl empty. It's gotten THAT bad. I HATE cleaning out the guinea pig cage with the huge oversized rat poop in it. And who the hell poops in pellets? That's so weird. Semi-soft pellets. That's not poop. That's like See's Candies. Stupid guinea pig poop.

I love my kids, but sometimes I wonder if I love them only because I'm supposed to love them. When you become a "mother", certain things come with the territory...like, um...actually loving your children.

Which brings me to my next topic. Suicide. I'm not going to sit here and lie to you, make all pretty like I've

6

never thought about it. I'm writing my inner most thoughts here. This is between me and my computer. OK, if you're reading this, I suppose it's between you and I also but you can't really stop me even if you wanted to. You don't know where I live. Although everyone is stalking everyone these days, so maybe you do know where I live. Can you really pay $9.99 to a website and get all of the information about someone? I HAVE NEVER DONE THAT. I'm just asking. Anyway, that's completely beside the point.

Don't get all freaked out just yet. I have *contemplated* suicide, just as every God loving American mother has done at one point or another during her daily laundry duty. Don't you sit there and tell me your life is all cheery. I'm soooo not going to listen to that garbage. Your life is wonderful, your husband is THE most loving and faithful man on the planet. Puke! Barf! You make me sick! That is not real life. REAL life is living day to day as a mom, trying to figure out exactly how you're going to make it through the sludge again. What the hell you can make for dinner that will taste the tiniest bit different from the previous night. We have ONE spice in our house. Garlic salt.

The old oven trick always sounded peaceful and non-violent to me, but I don't think that really works, does it? You just turn on your oven, open the door and close all the windows? Won't you just get hot and sweaty and be distracted from smelling that burning black charred stuff in the bottom of the oven that you should have cleaned out?

I really don't want to have to Google how to kill myself. Now THAT is depressing. Besides, I'm paranoid to Google anything because I feel like the FBI will come in and confiscate my hard drive. Completely irrational I know. It's got to be something that just comes naturally to me. And quick. Quick would be nice. Painless has its advantages. But there needs to be loads of blood. You see, I've envisioned my entire death...oh, about fifty times...the details are a little different each time, but the overall scene is quite consistent.

So, it's evening. The kids are with friends... because I'm sick, but not that sick. I want John to see the aftermath, but not the kids. First thing I do is turn on Nine Inch Nails. It's dark. It's dank. It just feels right for suicide music. I even have the song all picked out that will be playing with John comes home.

It's called "Everyday is Exactly the Same". So very fitting.

I believe I can see the future,
'Cause I repeat the same routine.
I think I used to have a purpose,
Then again, that might have been a dream.
Every day is exactly the same.
Every day is exactly the same.
There is no Love here,
And there is no pain.
Every day is exactly the same.

John comes home. The Nine Inch Nails music is loud. Uncomfortably loud. Of course he doesn't turn it down because he's a total asswipe wimp, afraid to make me mad.

"Honey?" he calls out. Like I'm his honey! Why the hell do married people call each other *honey?* Yuck! Sweetie? Disgusting. Pumpkin? Childlike. Married people suck.

It's dark and even though he is an unfeeling, uncommunicative, incapable of anything lump...he *knows* that something is amiss. "Denise?" He calls out. Maybe he'll get the hint that I won't be answering when he steps in the unusually huge pool of warm, sticky blood. His shoe slips. He loses his balance and has to check himself by holding onto the wall. Which is also covered in blood.

(Note to self: figure out how to get blood on the wall.)

Now that he has blood on his hands and shoes... he looks down to the dimly lit floor. Actually, not lit at all. Only the light of the blue full moon. (Yes, yes, I'm aware that I will need to check and see when exactly a full moon is coming. No one said suicide was a quick, easy accomplishment. At least not mine.)

Moonlight streams through the wood pane window. The window that I could never keep clean. The window with kid's fingerprints all freaking over it! Dead flies in the window sill. Dust from that windstorm eight months ago. Probably peanut butter too. Anyway, John follows the moonlight down to my

9

slumped, sideways body. The body placement is huge! Very important for maximum effect.

I want him to get sick. I want him to be absolutely stunned. I want him to suffer! I want him to drop to his knees, in more blood. (I might have to mix a little fake blood in with mine. I want a LOT of blood! Talking Saw XII bloodbath style.)

It takes a moment for his eyes to adjust to what he is seeing. Then, they focus. There I am. Donned in my mom apparel. A white (but now grayish-white due to my inability to use bleach correctly) t-shirt, khaki pants and an apron. All light colored for maximum blood soaked effect. My white slip on Converse tennis shoes are disgustingly red and splotchy.

He sees the gun. His stomach drops out of his colon and onto the blood-soaked floor. Then he sees my brains spewed all over the note. He HAS to pick up the note with my mom brains on it. Now THAT is sick. He has to move the brains aside to see what I've written. He will be touching the brains that HE drove to insanity! The brains that HE married! The brains that HE neglected so he could go on yearly fishing trips instead of to wine country like we used to.

I want him to FEEL the pain and guilt of what he did to me. I was a young, happy, creative person with a life. He chained me to the minivan, kitchen and washing machine. Those are the brains he will be forced to brush off…like he's brushed off the past five years of our marriage. Just brushed me off so HE could have a life.

The note:

Dear John,

Do you have any idea of the unhappiness that you have created in my heart? You used to care about me. You used to be my best friend. You used to cheer me up if I was unhappy. You used to say I was pretty. The past five years of my life have been nothing but purgatory. A life of work and punishment, with no thanks in return. You used me to have a clean house. A clean shirt. A clean bed. We haven't had sex for 5 years. What? Did you think I was happy? Did you think I was enjoying this? At least now you won't be able to go on your stupid fishing trips because you'll have three kids to raise. Not much fun time for you, eh? Not much dating either. What woman is going to want to date some beer gutted loser with three children under the age of 13. Now THAT is funny!

But then...my whole suicide fantasy comes crashing in around me. The moment I bring up the kids...the suicide dream cracks and shatters into thousands of pieces and I can't go on. I can't even get the scene pictured in my head for days. It's a problem.

Suicide is a very UN-motherly thing to do. I am so sucked into all the "mom guilt" that I, unfortunately, have to cross suicide off the list of viable options. It just sucks because really, it's the absolute most dramatic solution I have to my stupid life. Everything else just seems so lame. So done already.

I could just leave. Disappear. Change my name. Start over as a new person. Become a whore at a truck stop. Then, I look down to my "mom belly". If I'm being truthful with myself, I'm not exactly whore material. I could be the type of whore you see on COPS that sells blow jobs for $5.00. But that wouldn't exactly get me to the life I long for.

I could try to get on a game show or reality TV show. The pro being, of course, if I win, I get loads of cash and a new 15-minutes-of-fame-celebrity-life that would allow me to quite possibly leave this housewife taco stand. The con is, I am not perky enough to be on a game show. Game show contestants always seem so perky. Jumping up and down over everything. Screaming. I am not the "cheerleader" type. Grrrrr. Grumble.

I could be the *older* woman on Survivor, the one who never wears a bikini and they vote out first. What's the point of that? All those ridiculous casting videos trying to sell myself, only to be voted out first because I have a C-section scar too large to look good in a bikini. Urgh, the young bouncy girls on Survivor always make fun of the matronly older mom-type in the tankini. "Tankini" really? Who came up with that garbage. There aren't even bikinis in my "section" in department stores anymore. Bikinis are in the "Young Girl" area…Tankinis are sandwiched between the

Maternity wear and lingerie to "sculpt" your body. Sadness.

I could go to the police academy. Yeah, stop laughing. I've always thought it would be inspiring to be a detective and solve crimes. Put assholes behind bars. Get all Dexter vigilante. Purchase tons of plastic wrap and a few carefully sharpened knives. Think of the possibilities. I could plant drugs and frame my husband. Maybe I could murder our pool man and make John the fall guy. After all, I'd become an expert in evidence. OR I could go all Training Day and become a dirty cop and just plain kill John myself, while I smoke crack and play poker with gang members. I could hook up with a low-level meth dealer like Jesse. I could build my own Breaking Bad meth empire. But...I wouldn't know where to meet a low level meth dealer if I wanted to. It's a pretty brilliant cover though. No one would suspect PTA mom as someone with a meth lab.

Time, however, is not on my side. Just how long would that take, to go to the police academy and actually get to the point where they issue me a weapon? Too long. I am a desperate woman requiring desperate measures desperately quick. So you see why suicide seems like such a great option, and why I obsess over it.

If you think of any other options for me, please, don't hesitate to tweet me and let me know how I can get rid of this life and trade it in for a new one. @HouzeWife99. My lease is up, I am over mileage and

I want to smell the smell of new leather again. Surely it's not too late for me.

Denise, December 14th

Something red catches my eye. A flash. I slowly bring up my wrist into my vision. Blood. What have I done? Did I really do this? I didn't even know I did it? What? I want to kill myself so bad that I easily slit my wrist and didn't even feel it? If death is this painless, count me in. I did it. I really did it. I'm oddly proud of myself. I thought somehow I'd wimp out. You always wonder that about yourself. When it comes down to that moment, will you? Or won't you. I guess I do have balls...after all.

I am ending this torture. I am in shock that I forgot about the kids long enough to actually put the razor to my wrist. I am shaking, realizing I have to do the other wrist. And don't I have to go get into a warm bath or something? I seem to remember that's part of slitting your wrists. Not exactly sure why though.

Oh crap. You've got to be kidding me. WTF god! It's raspberry jam. From the kids' lunches this morning. I am such a sap! Although it does look like blood. And here I thought I was so powerful. So fearless. With raspberry jam on my wrist. This is SO something that would happen to me!

My marriage is screwed up. Married to a schmuck who only cares about himself. My suicide attempts end up being a messy peanut butter & jelly sandwich. My kids, well, I'm sure they love me, but they are so much damn work. If I happen to wake up with a little energy, actually got a good night's sleep, my kids suck it out by the end of breakfast. I am back to my wilting self in a bathrobe. The kids leave for school. John leaves for work. And I begin my Groundhog Day that I live over and over again. I can't even hear "I Got You Babe" by Sonny & Cher without having a facial twitch.

Then the decisions start. What am I going to do today? I see all the dishes in the sink. On the counters. Food crumbs all over the floor. Bills decorating the counters in various pile heights. Indoor plants dying, drooping downward, as I am. Dog pee on the floor. Homework that was forgotten. Crayons EVERYWHERE. Please don't just read over that last line, and think, "OK, crayons everywhere." No. I mean, CRAYONS #EVERYFUCKINGWHERE! On the floor. On the table. On the counter. In our chairs. In the living room. On the brick mantle. On the bar stool. In the refrigerator. On the garage floor. In the hallway. In our bed. In bathroom drawers. Flushed down the toilet. In the guinea pig cage. In the dog food bag. In the toaster oven. In the baking flour. In my purse. In John's suit pocket. Stuck in our dog's collar. In our pool. EVERYWHERE!!!!!

Surely they are one of man's most evil creations. They mate and multiply. Like rabbits. If they break, they leave their shredded selves so deeply in carpet, you can never remove them. It's their way of saying, "Fuck you, you broke me, now you'll have to see my desert sand, dandelion ugly ass color the rest of your life!"

If only I could be a crayon. Break. And leave my colorful self all over John's life, as a constant reminder of the art and sparkle he's sucked from me.

Now that I haven't actually slit my wrist, I sit here, with my only friend, a cup of coffee. I look out onto our yard of dog poop and wonder if today is the day I might possibly have enough guts.

It's 8:15 a.m. The kids are at school. John is on his way to work. My personal witching hour. The time when all my ugliest most horrible demons come out to taunt me. They make fun of the fact that I can never go through with "the plan". That day after day I pile clothes in our energy efficient front loader and press the button. My most creative thought is, "Hmm, this front loader could be a problem as I get older with my bad back." The whir of the washing machine and soapy water sloshing around often lulls me off to sleep. I can actually hear the demons chuckle as I try to decide between ordering pizza or making pasta for dinner. There is no change. It never changes. It's always the same. I often imagine that the day my kids leave for college is the day I will die. One way or another, I will die that day. It will be the greatest day of my life.

Denise, December 15th

I see sunlight over the top of the curtain. Am I dead? I never see sunlight coming in. It's always dark when I wake up. Maybe I'm in heaven? It really is pitiful that any variation in my day leads me to believe that I'm dead. Very much wishful thinking.

There are no clouds, no angels floating around and I see the basket of laundry I left next to my bedside. Most likely, this isn't heaven. But what's going on? I'm so disoriented. I hear the pig's voice.

Pig: "I think you overslept, the kids have to be at school in thirty minutes and they haven't had breakfast and aren't dressed".

Definitely NOT heaven. It appears that I have overslept. The annoying thing about over-sleeping for me is that I find myself completely disoriented when I wake up. It takes so much longer to understand where I am, what day it is and who I hate. Very aggravating. John knows this.

Me: "That can't be, my alarm was set for 6:00 a.m. It's always set for 6:00 a.m.," I manage as I pull myself out of bed. The goon speaks again.

Goon: "Well, it's 7:30, not 6:00."

Me: "Why didn't you wake me asshole? God forbid you do anything to help me or make my day a little easier, jerk!"

I totally snapped at him. I can't help it. When anything goes wrong, John IS the reason. And don't you tell me to read *The Proper Care and Feeding of Husbands* by Dr. Laura. Every time I even HEAR that title it automatically rots everything in my stomach and makes me want to puke. Dr. Laura is so pro-male, it's absurd. Who properly cares and feeds us women? We're supposed to prance around in skimpy outfits, kissing our men when they walk in the door, sip some wine and screw them...so THEY can be happy? What about us? How did we get to be the forgotten civilization?

One day the archaeologists of future societies will dig up aprons, rolling pins, and hand blenders and wonder what it was that caused millions of woman to die off the planet. They will probably find me, in a fetal position, perfectly mummified due to all the Comet cleanser in my body, gripping a mop. They will carbon date me back to 2016 and think how odd society was then. They will think how forward we were for having the first black president and yet they will wonder why women were treated as slaves, mopping, cleaning, and cooking. I hope in the future that women will be held in a higher regard and that robots will take over our hellish work. Really, what is a baby going to care if their own mother gags and holds back the vomit while changing their diaper, versus some metal robot? If only I had been born 200 years from now. Sigh.

John goes off on some rant asking me why he should wake me when all I will do is call him names. I happily respond.

Me: "Names? That is so laughable. *Asshole* and *jerk* are

not names. You WISH your name was Asshole. That would be such an improvement over your pansy ass name of "John". Your parents were so freaking creative with that one. They must have known what a genius you were going to be, maintaining computers for a law firm making seventyfucking thousand dollars a year! Total genius! Asshole would at least give you some credibility in the world. At least people might stop to wonder about you. Wonder how you got the name Asshole, wonder just how much of an asshole you really are. With "John" they just know you're a boring loser with no one who loves him!"

John gives me a very long look. I take a breath to spew more hate at him, but he turns and leaves. I win again. At least I can win in the verbal arena, because I have lost at life. As John has lost. I know neither of us would choose to relive this life again. How different we could be.

I am well aware that I shouldn't go off on John in front of the kids, but please believe me when I tell you, I cannot help it. He walks past me, and the volcano begins to rumble. The negativity that fills me when he is in the same room is stifling. I have a physical reaction to him. Perhaps I have become allergic to John. How funny would it be if I popped some Claritin, and suddenly John became my knight in shining armor? Not likely.

My friend Lynda says I should see a therapist. She believes that me telling some psychologist about what a rotten man I have suffered with over the years will somehow make things better. I do appreciate her positive outlook, but she is wrong. That is not going to change HIS self-centered ways and his total disregard for me.

Let's suffice it to say that today is no different from any day in my recent memory. I wake up. I'm miserable. I get the kids off to school with John. I'm miserable. I clean the house and write my thoughts down. I'm miserable. I pick up the kids from school and start dinner. I'm miserable. John comes home. I'm even more miserable. The kids go to bed. Still miserable. I climb into bed at the end of my day, next to my source of misery.

John, December 15th

I guess it's good that you can't just go get a divorce, like getting a latte, but it sure is maddening. I simply want to be free of the beast. I want to move on. I want to explore. I want to live. But there are so many steps. So many things that need to be decided. So many attorneys. Therapists that try to make our square marriage fit into a circular life. And there's the children. The part of this equation that leaves me filled with despair. I chose to have children. I chose to be a father. And now, I am a complete and utter failure. I am giving these children a very painful future. Filled with living at two houses. Filled with new people in their lives, calling themselves "stepdads" and "stepmoms". And worst of all, I am giving them the idea that if you make a mistake in choosing the person you are going to marry, you can always just get rid of them. I never, ever wanted to do that. I wanted to set the bar high. I wanted to show my children that not only is it possible to find someone to be with the rest of your life, I wanted to show them we could be happy. Utter failure.

Denise and I have shown them, if anything, what not to do. That is just beyond sad to me. But here we are, talking to attorneys, going to marriage counseling, and fighting every waking hour of our lives. This is what we show our children.

I've been talking to my great friend Keith, out on the golf course, and he told me to start writing down my thoughts regarding Denise. He thinks that me writing down how I feel about her will help something. I don't agree, but I promised him that I would give it a try. Personally, I feel like seeing my life written down will only make me feel worse than I already do. But since I am at the bottom of this life, and there is nowhere to go but up, I am trying.

How do I feel about Denise? Denise is mean. She is a mean and unapproachable human with ice, no, with *dry* ice running through her veins, and she is my wife. But, this woman is not the woman I married. There was a change, somewhere, but I couldn't really tell you when it happened. It was so gradual. Now, when I wake up every day, I realize the change is complete. There is not one shred left of the woman I married. I never saw Seth Brundle place my wife in a telepod, but

I am sure it happened. One day, when I was at work. Instead of a fly getting into the telepod with her, it surely must have been Saddam Hussein. I would bet my last dollar that Denise's DNA has totally and completely changed from when I first married her.

Let me tell you a little about the Denise that I married. There was no one like her. That sounds dumb and lame and what every guy would say about the woman they fall in love with, but I am so utterly sincere from the core of my being. Denise was like no one. She had a light and energy that others, men and women were instantly attracted to. She had a shine to her...she sparkled when she walked. I was so proud to have her on my arm when we went out. I never dreamed that someone so special would fall in love with me.

When we were first married, it was so 80's. So *Pretty in Pink*. So *Say Anything*. So black and white stripes. So pink hair. So *Dirty Dancing*.

Now, our marriage has deteriorated into one big 2016. So poor job market, so volatile stock market, so *Hunger Games*...where you try and kill someone who used to be your best friend. So next trendy terrorist group. So very depressing.

Most of all I am sad about what has happened to us. We were the couple that everyone thought would make it. We were the couple that people thought would sail with ease to our 50th wedding anniversary. I never looked at another woman, how useless would that have been? Denise was more than everything I ever wanted. I had found the person I was going to spend the rest of my life with.

I found literally everything sexy about that woman. How she still got pimples. God, she hated that with a passion, but not me. How her skin was so fair that she'd get freckles if she was out in the sun for ten minutes. She hated that too, thought they were age spots. But they would have always been freckles to me. Her walk was what you noticed first. It exuded happiness. How could walking exude happiness? Hers did. She had a spectacular flow to her hair, like there was always wind blowing through it, even during 100+ degree summers without a stitch of wind in sight.

Now, I feel nauseous prickles on the back of my neck when I see her. I begin sweating and have this immediate need to find a way out of the same location as her. I feel like an animal, trapped, frantic to find escape. I've been listening to this song lately (making sure Denise hears it) and...it's SO us. I torture Denise with it playing it out loud constantly. This song makes me feel a little less alone in the world. It's called "You Don't Know Me" by Ben Folds.

> *I wanna ask you*
> *Do you ever sit and wonder,*
> *It's so strange*
> *That we could be together for*
> *So long, and never know, never care*
> *What goes on in the other one's head?*
> *(You don't know me)*

You don't know me at all
You could have just propped me up on the table like a
mannequin
Or a cardboard stand-up and paint me (paint me
anything)
Any face that you wanted me.

Now I wonder if she ever knew me. It's truly difficult to remember a time when Denise and I got along. I've been listening to Dr. Laura quite a bit, partially because I know it drives Denise crazy, and partially because I believe Dr. Laura brings up some very good points. I hear plenty of husbands call in that are in my exact situation. Their wives have become different people over the years of marriage. It actually seems quite common.

So, perhaps with all our cancer and AIDS research, we should have someone looking into this epidemic. Could it be pollutants? Something in our environment that can cause a total metamorphosis in women? Something that causes the loving, sexy, fun woman you married to turn into a raging hell bitch? From hell. Raging. 24/7 of total and complete rage. Hellish rage.

What if there were a pill a woman could take, at the beginning of her marriage, that would keep her that same person - through buying a home, childbirth, getting wrinkles, husbands losing their hair, potbellies everything. No matter what changes took place in the marriage, the woman always stayed true to herself, who she was when the man first married her. If only.

Here's what really depresses me. When Denise and I get divorced, and eventually when I feel I'm ready to date again, I will try to find someone like Denise used to be.

Andrew, Denise and John's son

Hey so…yeah. All I see my parents do is fight. Yeah, that's pretty much it. They are experts at it though. My name is Andrew and I'm twelve. Does anyone care how I feel? Well, my parents suck. Big time. My sisters think they suck too. I don't think any of us will look back and think that we had happy childhoods. That's really crappy. There's not really anything we can do. We're pretty much stuck. Being at school is the best part of my life, because I don't have to listen to them. They hate each other so much. I wonder day after day why they ever got married. I've never seen them happy together.

I can tell you right now, I will never get married. Ever. What a ridiculous and pointless thing. You may say I'm young and I'll change my mind over time, but I know I won't. I *know* I won't. I know, because I will never do this to my kids. It's pretty much hell. I'd rather be an orphan, living in foster care, than hear them every day of my life screaming at each other. I really wish they had divorced sooner, to spare us years of pain. I guess it's more painful for my sisters, they cry a lot more than I do. Me? I'm just angry. I'm angry at my parents that they only think of themselves. That they could care less about us, and that we have to witness their fighting every day. I almost think my mom enjoys the fighting. She is REALLY good at it.

My sister, Amber, also says she'll never get married. Good for her. She's smart. Molly, my youngest sister, just thinks Mom and Dad picked the wrong person and thinks if you pick the RIGHT person, marriage can be happy. But, she's 6. She doesn't know anything. She doesn't know what I know…that marriage is never a happy situation. Hopefully she'll learn the truth before she grows up and makes a huge mistake. Marriage = never happy! Period!

That's how I feel. Whatever.

Denise, December 16th

Lovely. Nothing better than going to some psyche session with my loser husband because our attorneys told us we have to. I really have a positive outlook about these sessions, really feel like we can accomplish something, make progress, find a common ground NOT! What a load! My "feelings"…??? I'll tell you what my feelings are! I feel that my husband is an ass wipe wimp who should probably be gay because he just wasn't made to make any woman happy!

Here's a little sample of what's going down:

Therapist: "I hope we've made some progress since last week. Have you all tried saying positive things to each other, reinforcing the good things that we concentrated on about your marriage last time?"

Me: laugh

John: smirk

Psychologist: "Does that mean yes?"

Me: laugh

John: smirk

Psychologist: "Ok, I'll assume that's a yes, which is good. We need to reinforce anything positive, no matter how small. By concentrating on the positive, ONLY, it will begin to chip away at the years of negative thinking."

Me: laugh

John: smirk

Me: "If I were going to say something positive about John, it would be that he is the BEST asshole I've ever met."

John: "And if I were going to say something positive about you, dear wife, it would be that you have turned into the most hateful, numero uno, queen bitch on the face of the planet."

We both turned to the therapist who came back with something along the lines of that wasn't exactly what he was looking for. Then, he went off in a completely different direction, telling us that we are not alone, that people have come back from where we are, don't lose hope...all that kind of B.S. Huh? Marriage counseling is worthless. Completely. But me, always the martyr, go along with it because my attorney says it will look like I "tried" to keep the marriage together. He also thinks I can get more money out of John, and alas, the real reason for putting myself through this torture.

So I'm sitting here at the therapy session, and my mind just wanders. It's not something I can control. It happens. I figure smack in the middle of a marriage counseling session is a pretty good place to lose myself in some great thoughts, because hell, the alternative of sitting there working on my "marriage" is just dumb.

I picture John after our divorce. He's going all midlife crisis, doing things he's never done before. Getting his hair dyed. Wearing bike shorts with his rolls of gut spilling out over the top. Getting waxed. Trying out for Survivor. He thinks that by doing something crazy, and daring, he'll be really living his life. Doing something that he's always wanted to do, but never could, because *I* was holding him back. Oh yeah, he'll blame me for every negative thing that ever happened to him. I can see him in his audition tape, telling Jeff Probst how he's only started to live now that he's divorced from the shrew that was keeping his life hostage. Probst will feel bad for him, saying they picked John to be on Survivor because of his moving audition tape. Because the producers of Survivor wanted to give John a new lease on life.

How humiliating that he's going to be that "old guy". Ha! All the young kids, with their abs & boobs, will talk behind his back about him. His grizzly bear hairy back, and the way he has no ass in his swimming suit! Said swimming trunk will surely fall off in every water challenge due to the fact that there is no ass to hold it up. I can see him giving his ration of rice to some hot, young cleavage, doh, I mean GIRL, thinking he has a shot with her. While she tells the camera "I'm going to use everything I've got out here, and if it means flashing my boobs to some old fart to get his rice, then more power to me!"

Or better yet, he'll trip, fall on his face, cut his nose, and that will get huge and infected by some malaria filled bug. Puss and white oozy stuff will run out of it. There will be LOTS of close ups of John's nose on national television. HD television. (No woman will want him after seeing his puss oozing nose on HD television!) Medical will have to come and assess his oozing puss filled nose, only to tell him he'll have to leave the game...after two days! Ahhh, this makes me laugh out loud. The therapist and John look at me. I really wonder what they were talking about. My laugh must have been very out of place considering the look on their faces. Who cares?

John

I wonder what the hell she is laughing at over there. I mean, what the hell goes on in that woman's head? Here we're talking about why we were attracted to each other when we were first dating, a time that is really very special to me. A time in my life when I was truly happy. A time that I cherish. And she laughs. Wow. She's a piece of work.

I'd love to be in her head for a day. Love to try to understand how she can be as mean as she is, with no remorse. Does she enjoy it? She probably never loved me the way I loved her. It was probably all a joke to her from day one. I wonder why she really did marry me?

I wonder if she ever felt any kind of love for me? She is a mean, mean woman.

I wonder, when Andrew was born, and we were both crying, holding each other, and holding Andrew...she said she never loved me more than that moment. I wonder. Was it true? Did she mean it? Or was it just the rush of childbirth, caught in the moment that caused her to say that? I wonder about it all. Every moment she ever said anything loving or nice to me, it's all playing back in my head now. Over and over. Sort of taunting me for ever believing it. It's really humiliating.

Denise, December 17th

So. Here we go again. Kids are at school. John scurried out the door like the little hamster ass that he is, off to work. Going to go run on his little wheel all day to get his little sunflower seed. And I'm here. Sitting in the kitchen, with the sexiest man I know, my cup of coffee. My cup of coffee has more balls than John will ever have. My cup of coffee is strong, smooth and makes me feel good. SO much more than I can say for John. Hot. Easy to hold. I'm excited to see my cup of coffee every morning. Man, I really should have married a cup of coffee instead of John. I wonder what my kids would look like. Probably look like little Starbucks muffins. Or cake pops. I'd just come out to the kitchen in the morning and see all my kids lined up in the glass display case, looking all sweet and yummy.

Boy, I'm really losing it. I don't know how much longer I can go on. Living here, in the same house with him. I am a miserable woman. I can't even enjoy my kids because I'm so on edge about John all the time. What am I doing to myself? To my kids? My whole life seems to revolve around making John miserable. But I can't help it! I can't seem to get motivated to do anything except make him miserable. Make him squirm. I live for it. I don't want to do laundry. I don't want to clean the kitchen. I don't want to help Molly with homework. I want to make John miserable. Actually, for not having a degree in 'making your husband miserable', I think I do pretty well at it. Why can't I stop myself? I have no self-control. It's a strange sensation, to have anger take such a hold of you, that you no longer control your life. Anger controls me. I know this. But I am just banking on the hope that after I divorce that hairy little gerbil ass, I will go back to being a normal person. Able to function. Able to have fun and enjoy life. Able to enjoy my kids.

It's really unbelievable that the dogs know exactly when I'm at my lowest. Exactly when to poop in the house on my shag rug. I love that shag rug. I used to do my yoga on it. But now the dogs have pooped exactly every foot and a half, over the entire surface of my shag rug, so I can no longer lie on it to do yoga. I have to put a towel down first. Which is really annoying. Because if any part of my body goes off the towel, I feel like I need to shower to get the dog poop remnants off. Blech! Then I'm so distracted by the possible poop contamination, I can't do my yoga. I wouldn't be surprised if John taught the dogs to poop on my rug. That was my happy rug. Everything in this house has changed. Every single thing.

Here's yet another annoying thing about my life. It's mid-December. I have to start shopping for Hannukah and Christmas presents for the kids. Can I just say that is about the LAST thing I want to do? John won't be buying any presents for the kids, that always falls on me. I wish this was over already. How absolutely painful to celebrate the holidays in this depressing home.

Denise, December 18th 7:55 a.m.

Lovely. Yet another morning waking up next to waffle ass. Just what I've always dreamed of, waking next to a spongy assed man that I hate. I greet him like any loving wife should.

Moi: "Hi Dick"

Dick: "Real nice Denise."

Moi: "Oh, poor baby doesn't like being called Dick. OK, good morning Huggies ass wipe!"

Huggies Ass Wipe: "Why don't you just shut your mouth? You really are more attractive that way".

Moi: "Oooh, the black hole of all assholes makes a comeback! Are you actually trying to be mean to me?"

Hahahahah!!! I have a very hearty chuckle over this.

Black Hole of Asses: "Denise, just give it a rest. You've called me every name in the book, I'm really immune to it all now."

Moi: "Immune? You've become immune to name calling? Wow! You're amazing tiny baby penis man!"

Tiny Baby Penis Man: "Do you think I'm going to cry or something?"

Moi: "One can only hope. If you weren't such a moronic excuse for a man, an embarrassment to the male species, a no brain, small dicked, disgustingly hairy, beer gutted LOSER...you might actually understand how horrible and foul you are! You might see how others see you, a pig-like, pig-sounding, pig-looking human that no one cares about. People at your work make fun of you. The kids and I make fun of you. Your friend, Keith, your great fishing trip buddy makes fun of you. Everyone thinks you're this huge pig joke. NO one has ever taken you seriously. You're along for the ride in life John. People keep you around because you're fun to make fun of. I'm done with you. Everyone is done with you. You have no friends. You have no wife. No one loves you. You ARE a pig. "

John gives me that look, the one that *almost* sends a tiny twinge of remorse through me, but not quite. The look where I know I've won. I know that stung. The look that tells me that *I* have the power. The look that I know I've hurt him. Success.

John: "Denise, you are a horrible person. I really can't believe that this is who you are now. You're just mean. You're the ugly one."

Me: "I'm ugly? Ha! What a total joke! Where have YOU been the last 5 years John! WHERE? Off on fishing trips. Off with 'the guys'. Sitting on your ass downstairs watching golf! Off in the garage...Off ANYWHERE except where I was. What's uglier John? A wife who calls her husband names? Or a husband that completely neglects his wife for YEARS!? A husband that would rather sit his ass in front of a television than talk to me. A husband that would rather tinker with a dripping faucet than help me make dinner. A husband that would rather not miss the Super Bowl than go out to dinner on our anniversary. THAT is ugly John! YOU are the ugly one here. I may call you a few fifth grade names, but YOU are the one who has ruined us! Yes, I hate you with as much passion and hate as any human could muster. But you deserve every ounce of hate I have John. You took something beautiful, completely neglected it, and it turned into this. YOU! My name calling didn't do this to us John. YOU did!"

John: "Nice try Denise! SO damn easy to put the blame on me. You're really looking for the easy way out. I'm NOT giving it to you! WHY?! Why did I choose to tinker with the leak, watch the game, or go on trips with the guys? WHY? Because you were no fun anymore! You changed! You were this fun, beautiful, happy person! Now you are raging at me every waking moment of every day. Nothing is right. Nothing is good enough. You complain and nag about every little thing I do throughout the day. Who would want to be with that? NO ONE, that's who! Who wants to be around someone pointing out every little flaw of theirs? Every misstep? I dreaded every day coming home to you. Knowing that this was my life. I stepped in that door and knew I would begin to hear everything I had done wrong during the day. How I dropped the kids off at the wrong time. Made their lunches wrong. Didn't pay the right bills. Didn't call the doctor. Didn't have the trash cans at the right spot on the curb. Every fucking thing I did was wrong according to you! You tell me, WHY would I want to be around that?"

At this point, I see Andrew come to the doorway and semi-hear him say something about them being late for school, but I can't concentrate on him. I notice that John also ignores Andrew. I cannot believe what I just heard. I cannot believe that in his heart, he truly believes this is all my fault. I am so floored and so shocked. Utterly in shock. I have thought that at least we have been on the same page, understanding that him neglecting me has been the cause of our demise, but no. He sincerely believes this is all my fault.

Me: "I didn't think it was possible for me to be any more disgusted in you than I was. Didn't think it was possible. But John, you're a sick man. You need help. You have a mental problem. Your facts are warped, you don't even understand what has happened here. It's like you've had one giant black out from drinking. Maybe you need to be in a hospital."

John: "What? What are you saying Denise! Like a mental hospital? There's nothing wrong with my memory. YOU'RE the one that is delusional! YOU are the self-centered bitch with no regard for anyone but yourself. YOU are the one that doesn't care if I or the kids live or die!"

At that moment Molly comes to the door crying. Screaming at us to stop. But I go over, gently push her out the door, and close it. It feels wrong to do that, but I have no power over choosing to stay involved in this argument. It's like a drug, like an addiction. I know that I should stop, get the kids to school, and stop this fight. But I can't stop. Am I continuing to win? Maybe, I don't even know. I just know that I can't stop.

Me: "I care if the kids die…you? Not so much. So you're right. I don't care if you die. Why would I? You're just like some guy off the street that I don't even know. You are not the man I fell in love with. Not even close."

John: "Well there's one thing we agree on. The woman I married was lovable. She was beautiful. She was my world. *You* are a complete raging maniac that spews nothing but hatred."

Me: "I cannot stand you. Get out of here."

John: "Who would have thought, we agree on two things. I can't stand you either".

John leaves the room and I assume he is taking the kids to school. I just feel numb. I don't feel like doing anything. I don't even cry. I just sit here, looking around our bedroom for about forty five minutes. I don't feel anything when I look at the pictures of the kids on the dresser. Don't feel anything when I look at the honeymoon picture of John and I. Don't feel anything when I look at our bed, that we've slept in together for years. What an odd sensation. After all that hatred, I just sit here. Oh, I have hate in my heart for him, but it isn't that crazy, screaming hate. It is turning, morphing into calculated hate. A more intelligent hate. A hate that I can do great damage with.

The idea comes to me. Suddenly it is in my head. Like it has always been here. After days of waking up to dread, coffee and yelling, I finally have a plan. Today, I will go shopping. I know what you're thinking. You're thinking I'm going "girl shopping". The kind where women make themselves feel better by buying themselves pretty things. No, not that kind of shopping. I'm talking the kind of shopping that can ruin one's credit. I'm talking charging over the limits on ALL your credit cards. I'm talking charging so much that "someone" will NEVER get out of debt with his $70,000 a year job. I'm talking the kind of shopping trip that makes your fucking FICO score drop like a ton of bricks off the U.S. Bank Building in downtown Los Angeles. It's really a win-win situation for me. I ruin John's pristine credit, something he holds near and dear to him, AND I get to buy a ton of stuff including Christmas and Hannukah presents for the kids. Maybe a little bauble thrown in there for myself wouldn't hurt! This is my day. I plan on savoring every minute.

I get every credit card I can find, even the ones in John's underwear drawer that aren't activated yet. He keeps them in there because he doesn't think criminals will want to sift through his hole-y and torn Costco underwear to get loot. Brilliant man I'm married to, what can I say. I move the striped boxers over to reveal Crate & Barrel. Pottery Barn. Macy's. American Express. Our ATM Visa card. JC Penny's. Discover. And finally, last but not least, Capitol One. My favorite. No hassle. They're the only credit card company that hasn't arbitrarily raised our interest rate. But still, when it comes to screwing John over, I do not play favorites. Every card gets to play.

Yeah, so maybe I'm screwing myself too. What? You think I didn't think of that? That my credit score will also tank? Of course I know that. However, I don't care the way John cares. THAT is the difference. John had a major credit faux pas early on in life. It took him years to get his credit clean after college. Then, he became completely anal about it. He'd make credit card payments before he'd tuck the kids into bed. It would be 10:30, the kids would be half asleep waiting for daddy to come tuck them in, but NO! John just HAD to make those payments. He is credit obsessed! He loves his credit score of 840 more than he loves me. No doubt. That is why this is the absolute most perfect mean revenge to take on him. Couldn't be more perfect.

My head feels foggy from this morning's fight. Like a hangover. Not a head splitting drunk hangover. Just one that leaves that dull ache in your head. Behind your eyes. I'm exhausted. Exhausted from fighting. From hating. From him. I'm banking that my little stunt will be the final straw for him and cause him to move out. He's been avoiding it due to "finances", but just wait. I bet you this will push him over the edge.

I love Los Angeles. This city has so much to offer. I love that it's spread out. I love that you can go to so many different parts of town, so many flavors, yet you are still in Los Angeles. John and I, before we had kids, would start at one side of town splitting drinks and hors d'oeuvres at restaurants from the ocean to Hollywood. We'd spend hours driving all over this city. Today, I plan on heading west, Santa Monica is my first stop. Third Street Promenade. From there I'll head east, Century City, Beverly Hills, Hollywood, then perhaps some downtown shopping. Chinatown? Olvera street?

There's tons of traffic on the 10 freeway this morning, which I know, is pretty shocking. Actually, it's surprising when there is no traffic on L.A. freeways. Traffic is like an old recliner. Warm and comfy. Familiar. I never mind traffic. Where are all these people going? I love looking over into other cars as I inch along. Making up stories as I go about who they are. What they do for a living. Are they happily with someone? Or are they like me? Stuck in a dead end relationship with a dead end spouse?

It's a crisp December day and I have my big wool coat on. Completely unnecessary, but as we all know in L.A., if you want to wear a nice, big, warm winter coat, you just have to go balls to the wall and do it because if you wait for that 30 degree snow day, you'll have a long wait ahead of you. It is slightly embarrassing though when you're wearing your big wool coat and kids walk past you in shorts and tank tops.

You'll need to forgive me, everyone copes with driving in Los Angeles in different ways. Some listen to music or talk radio. Some use it as time to conduct business, constantly on the phone, making deals. Some just use driving so they can shoot out their windows. (Joking. Well, sort of joking.) I can't conduct even small conversations on cell phones, as inevitably they cut out and I miss half of what the other person is saying then feel like an idiot because I keep asking "What?", "Huh?", "Could you repeat that?", "You cut out!" OR... I just end up saying "Wow..." "Right", "Totally!"...and giving a small laugh, hoping to God that laughing was appropriate at that moment! My method for traffic coping is letting my mind wander. Boy, does my mind wander. I can go from thinking about hating John, to mangoes, to fire-eaters, to dandruff in less than ten seconds. You have to have a mind like mine to appreciate just how lost in thought I can become. It has made dealing with L.A. traffic much easier, time just flies by.

As I drive along, I imagine John after our divorce. Dating. Why I have images of him in my head with other women, God knows. I'm just a salt-in-the-wound kinda gal. I think he'll stay true to the man code and go younger. A teacher maybe. No, a teacher would be too smart for him. A teacher would read books. No, he's going to want a younger woman who fishes, barbecues and watches sports. Hmmm. That sounds like he may just need to date a lesbian. Hell, I may date a lesbian. I sure as hell don't want any more men! I wonder how many women have gone over to the lesbian side after divorcing a man. I would venture to bet there would be quite a few! But here's my lesbian issue...I don't want a "man" lesbian. One that acts and dresses manly. I don't want anyone even remotely resembling a man! I have had it with MEN. I get a little twinge when I see the "Men's" sign on restroom doors! Men! HAD IT!

Can you have two girly lesbians together? Does it work that way? Note to self: try and think of gay friend that I can ask if it's kosher for two girly lesbians to hook up. While I'm at it, I think I'd have to ask, just for the knowledge, if two manly lesbians ever hook up. Hmmm. If a woman is a manly sort of lesbian, then why would she be attracted to another manly lesbian? Wouldn't she just like a man? I wonder if manly lesbians find some men attractive. But they just HATE men so they don't bother. Maybe it's the penis that they hate. Preach it sister! So many questions to ponder in this crazy life of mine.

There's just something about the Third Street Promenade in Santa Monica. I wouldn't say it's the GREATEST place to shop on earth, but it offers surroundings that indoor malls cannot. The stores and shops are along an actual street that they blocked off in the sixties for pedestrian shopping. How brilliant is that? They should block off a few freeways and perhaps some churches too. Turn them into shopping. I'm all for more shopping. The morning air in Santa Monica is cool, a little misty and the smell of the ocean is undeniable. My favorite times for shopping at the Third Street Promenade are either right when everything opens, so it's not crowded - you can even walk fast enough to the point of getting some brisk exercise - OR, you have to go on a Saturday night. Wall to wall people, street performers including acrobats, jugglers, hip hop dancers, and there will always and forever be someone preaching about how we're all going to hell because we have lost our faith. They usually have some sign, with scripture written on it saying "Believe in Jesus, before it's too late or you will be damned." Which brings me to another thing I hate in life besides John. Pressuring people by fear into doing what you want them to do. Who came up with something that lame? To me, religion is a choice you make out of love, not fear. So don't be telling me I'll be damned to the eternal fires with Satan if I don't do what you want me to, because I'm the kind of person that will just happily walk into the fire with Satan just to spite you! The really incredible part is that some people are so weak, they are influenced by fear. Sad but true.

I park and head over to the shopping. On my way, I catch the eye of a homeless woman. Her eyes. I keep walking but her eyes stay with me. They are clear and sparkling, surrounded by a dirty, withered face. Those are the eyes of the president of a company, or a professor, or a star athlete. They are not the eyes of a destitute homeless woman. How did those eyes get into that body? It doesn't fit, I have to go back and see those eyes again. Those eyes, I'm positive do not belong in that body. As I walk back towards her, she already knows I'm coming and is meeting my stare. I probably stand there for about five minutes, just staring into her eyes. We never say a word, but I am compelled to give her John's ATM card with a slip of paper that has the pin on it. She doesn't smile or say thank you, and she doesn't need to. She doesn't really need any help from me, because I'm sure that she's independently wealthy with a high position in a corporation somewhere. I have to tell myself things like that, otherwise it's too painful for me to actually think about people living on the street. We just lump them into a category "homeless" so we can talk about them like they're from another planet, without accepting the responsibility that WE created this problem. John and I always did what we could for homeless people. I guess we had at least that ONE thing in common.

Where to begin? I see a young girl with an angular hair cut opening the door of Anthropologie. Great, I'll start with a little "ME" spending. I love this store, so many things to look at - from clothing, to cabinet knobs, to candles, to odd big jewelry, to dog sweaters. Clearly I need sixty dollar tiny doggie sweaters, knitted out of angora. See, if I buy practical things today, John just might forgive me. I don't want to be forgiven.

Well, that has got to be the ugliest necklace I've ever seen. $198.00? I must not get fashion anymore. At all. It's on a chain, and has four flowers on it, made out of metal, a brown one, a yellow one, a red one and a white one. Really ugly flowers. Who wears this crap for $198.00? This ugly necklace needs to be included in my revenge shopping spree, it's just weird. OH, and that one over there...it's called a "Fluidity Necklace"! OMG...THAT is funny! This one sells for $138.00 and is purple and looks like a crab claw with two big clam shells hanging off the claw. Yep, need that too.

My time at the Third Street Promenade pretty much goes like that. I see something ugly, or strange, or totally unnecessary to daily life, and buy it. Anything that I think John would disagree with, I need. After all, let us not forget why we have gathered here today. For John. Because the man I once loved forgot all about me. Forgot what we had. Forgot I was special. Forgot that we always said that WE would come first with each other. Not the kids. Not work. Not friends. It was us against the world, and he forgot.

Small things that I buy I carry, but larger things I just have shipped. I have never splurged like this in my life! I feel like a celebrity. Isn't that what they do? Have everything shipped to themselves? I can tell the people ringing me up think I must be very important to have my items shipped across town, when I live 40 minutes away (two hours in traffic). Suddenly I wish I had dressed the part, rather than sweat pants and my Old Navy mom t-shirt. Whatever. I'll just act like the wealthy incognito woman. Certainly I can act "incognito". I've been "incognito" to John for five years. "Incognito" in the bedroom is my specialty. I don't even think he knew I was female anymore. He probably felt I was just a human, genderless, put on earth to make him miserable. Little did he know, that a few kind words, a hug now and then, a "thank you for doing my laundry" would have gone SO far. To be unappreciated for so long would make anyone miserable.

Enough of my misery, this is about revenge! Next stop...Century City! Century City is a bit more upper crust than Third Street Promenade. Less beachy people, more Mercedes people but still fun shopping. I have fond memories of heading to Century City as a child and going to Harry's Bar & American Grill for dinner. The waiters always paid so much attention to kids. I'll never forget those outgoing, good looking Italian waiters. Ahhhh.

I had an odd experience at the old Century Plaza Hotel once. My parents took me and my friend Maria out to dinner there one time. Maria and I decided to go up to the top floor of the hotel to look at the view. Problem was, there was no way to see the view once we got up there. Only hotel room doors. We walked up and down the long hall, looking for a way to see the view, when a security guard stopped us and asked us what we were doing. Leave it to teenagers to not tell the truth. We said we were lost, which in hindsight, was pretty stupid. We should have just said we were trying to see the view. Long story short, the security guard thought we were hookers! Teenage hookers? I guess it happens, I just didn't think I had the hooker look. We had to show him our private (girls only) Catholic school I.D. cards. Only then did he think we possibly weren't hookers. He followed us down to the lobby, where we found my parents and got in their car. Completely embarrassing! My only hooking experience. At least it was in Century City, in a nice hotel, not along Santa Monica Boulevard.

I hit Bloomingdales at warp speed! Spock would be proud. Shoes. Kid's clothing. Housewares, new dishes, knife set, Calphalon pans. Did you know clothing designers now make China? Vera Wang. They also make bedding, Calvin Klein and Donna Karan! Gotta have me some of that! I haven't been shopping in stores other than Target for so long, who knew?

I see a lovely bedding display, you know, where the bed is all made up with about forty pillows, not a wrinkle on the sheets, no dog hair or food crumbs either. I want to lie down and feel what a bed that clean feels like, but then, my overactive mind takes control and flashes an image of John with his new girl. Frolicking and laughing on the bed. So happy that I was out of the picture. He looks like a different man. Happy. Interested in her. Interested in sex. Interested in what she is thinking. And why are her boobs that big? Why is my mind so cruel to me? Ugh. I shake my head quickly to get rid of that image.

Back to shopping. I decide to go to Brookstone. Why is that damn massage chair always so alluring? I mean I've sat in it many times. Every time I awkwardly lie down on it, it's a let down. Hard lumps come up from behind you jamming into your bones until you can't take the pressure anymore. You look for the controls to turn down the pressure but for some reason the one button that controls the thing is too complex to understand so you get out of the chair as quick as you can. And yet, every single time I go into the store, something draws me to sit in that stupid chair.

Today is no different. Thankfully, no one is around. The employees all seem to be at the back of the store. I slip my mom body into the black and slightly worn massage chair. I press the button six times until I hear the chair revving up. Buzzzzzzz. I lay back thinking this time will be different. I can really use a massage about now. Hard lumps spike up into my spine and two harder lumps shoot into the back of my neck. It is so painful I let out a scream. "OUCH!" I open my eyes to see one of the young male employees standing over me asking me if I am OK.

As I open my mouth to tell him I'm fine, a spike shoots up in the back of my neck and all that comes out is "Glah". It must concern him as he reaches for my hands to help pull me out of the torture machine. I reach my arms up and grab onto him. I am halfway up out of the chair as I move my foot over to get it on the ground when our grips slip. That damn Bath & Body Works coconut lotion that I sampled! I fall back onto the upper part of the recliner which makes it tip back and causes me to go rolling off onto the display floor. By this time there are a total of three young male Brookstone employees grabbing at various parts of me to get me upright.

"Are you OK ma'am?" one little blond fellow asks me, his name "Daniel" pinned on his pocket.

I am a little out of breath when I respond. I mean this is the most cardio I've done in a while. "Yes Daniel I'm fine, just too much coconut lotion." Apparently that confuses him as he looks to his friend. The friend, "Raj" makes a motion with his hands as if he is grabbing something, then that something slips from his hands. I'm just so humiliated. A crowd has formed and to my horror, I look down and my t-shirt has shifted upwards and about two inches of my mom belly is exposed! MY GOD! I grab my packages and race for the large opening to the mall...must...get...to the...opening...

I turn around to see the three Brookstone boys running after me, but I make it to the mall opening before they can reach me. I wander back off into the mall for a while. I can't stop thinking how I probably ruined the idea of marriage for those nice young men...that they were thinking "Urgh I'm never getting married, look what happens to them after you marry them!" Maybe I can be the poster woman for marriage prevention. I'll just hold a mop and wear my normal jam stained clothing and have my mom belly seep out over my pants. Just think how many men I could deter from marriage. Sigh.

Enough with Century City. I'm just feeling foggy. I don't feel sick, but I definitely don't feel right. Maybe this whole revenge thing doesn't agree with me. Or, maybe I'm just hungry. I drive down Santa Monica Boulevard to Beverly Hills. I mean, what's a shopping spree if I don't hit Beverly Hills, right? As I pull into the parking lot, I have to stop to let these girls walk SLOWLY in front of my car. Oh, it's Paris Hilton! Hmm. She's pretty cute. She had this show on TV a couple of years ago. She was interviewing random people to be her new best friend. For some reason I always thought that Paris would have picked me if I were on that show. Ewww, she's with some pretty skanky girls. What even happens to boobs that big once you unhook them from their bras at night? They must come crashing down and hit you in the gut and knock the wind out of you. (At least that's what I tell myself. Have to make myself feel better about my A cups.) Paris glances at me, and then walks on. I think she knows. She knows she'd rather be with me, shopping her ass off. But alas, she has an image to uphold, and being seen with a mom in Target pants, probably not so hot for the image.

I love the Crate & Barrel in Beverly Hills. I'd like to live there. It's so bright and open. Everything looks so clean. Here's what I've always wanted. A dining room set of my own. Not one that we found in someone's trash one year, when the trash company does a free pick up of large items. John thought he'd scored in a major way by snagging someone's old dining set. He painted it brown and we used that for several years before his parents took pity on us and gave us their 1970's dining set. Sort of bamboo-ish looking. It was "OK" but I've never had a dinning set of my own. Today is my lucky day!

The fellow that helps me smells SO good. I just keep breathing in his smell coming off his freshly pressed shirt. He could sell me anything. And he does. I ask him what my max is on our Crate & Barrel credit card. I give him some story about how our friend's daughter is having her wedding at our house, and we need to refurnish several rooms. He is sooooooooo helpful. That smell...it is slightly like Ralph Lauren Polo cologne. Which is a huge part of my sexual make-up. When I was 12, my friend and I watched *Endless Love* starring Brooke Shields on cable. But first, we sprayed ourselves with my dad's Polo cologne. Please don't ask why. It made perfect sense then. Ever since that moment, every time I even see that green bottle, it stirs my loins like pancake batter. Ahhhhhh. Needless to say, this Crate & Barrel salesman scored when he asked "May I help you?" Finally a dining room set of my own. Too bad I won't be able to enjoy it with my family. Won't be able to have holiday dinners on it together. It's just a table of revenge. Sad.

I walk around Beverly Hills for a while, looking for Paris, but I never see her again. I don't know why I feel like Paris would have some answer for me. Maybe she would have some information or insight that would make this all better. What a weird idea. There are a lot of beautiful people shopping and eating and talking and walking. Same old, same old...Los Angeles.

I get back in my car and head east along Santa Monica Boulevard again. I'm so hungry. So foggy. It is becoming really difficult to even make decisions. It feels as if someone else is making the decisions about where I go. As if something or someone has taken over. I really don't think I am in control. Probably not the best case scenario to be behind the wheel of an automobile, but hey, 98% of people in Los Angeles shouldn't be behind the wheel of a car, so join the crowd.

I have to pull over. I am feeling very woozy and lightheaded. I sit here for awhile looking straight ahead until some happy, bright young man walking by catches my eye. He smiles at me with a smile so strong that the corners of my mouth involuntarily draw north. He points to the store I am parked in front of...Cake and Art. He walks into the store. I follow him. Definitely I could use some cake and art. The smell is pure heaven. It fills my lungs and stomach with a sweet fulfilling aroma. I do love sweets. I think it shows in my 'mom butt' too. Man, the smell in this place is just incredible. There are cakes and cupcakes and chocolate and just YES. I want. I need. Mom want. Mom need. I order. I eat. I order another cupcake. I eat. I notice I'm the only female in the store and certainly the worst dressed. The young man who came in before me sits down at my table. I can't help but smile at him. He's so cute and fresh and clean. He smiles back. How curious he just starts talking to me.

Young Man: "Do you like your cupcake?"

I just nod due to the fact that my mouth is too full. I finish chewing my bite.

Me: "Are you gay?"

He nods and smiles again. I smile back.

Me: "Are all gay people as happy as you?"

He nods and smiles again.

Me: "Could I become gay?"

Young Man: "You want to be gay?"

Me: "Maybe. You just look happy and content. I want to be happy and content and this whole being married thing isn't cutting it for me."

Young Man: "Ahhhhh, marriage. How long have you been married to him?"

Me: "Long enough to turn me from a hot young babe, into this."

I look down and my mom-ness, motioning with my hand.

Young Man: "You're still hot."

Then he smiles at me again.

Me: "You are the nicest young man I have ever met. And you're so clean."

The young man laughs.

Young Man: "I think married people forget. Forget themselves. Forget to take time. Life becomes about bills, karate lessons and what to make for dinner."

Me: "How do *you* know that?"

Young Man: "My parents. But there's always hope. You can't lose hope."

I just smile at his enthusiasm, because I know in my heart, all hope is gone. I don't want to crush this sweet young man's dreams or his hope.

Me: "Can I ask you a question?"

He nods.

Me: "You know how, with lesbians, one might be the more manly one in the relationship, and one might be the more girly one?"

He laughs and motions with his hand for me to continue.

"Well, I was wondering, do two girly girls ever hook up?"

Young Man: "Honey, you're not becoming a lesbian. Seriously, you would be like the worst lesbian I've ever seen, girly or not girly. You need another cupcake to fulfill your binge and you need to go home and work this out."

He buys me another cupcake then gives me his card before I leave. A hair dresser!

Young Man: "You need to come and see me, I will show you that you're still hot!"

He walks me out to my car and gives me a hug. A hug! This clean young man, that doesn't even know me. Random act of kindness. I'm sure his Karma quota has been filled for the month. This town is kind of strange. There are so many people here and yet hardly anyone just starts up conversations with strangers. I feel like in the old days, people used to strike up conversations, they used to care about strangers and their stories. Today, people are so much more selfish and into only themselves, afraid to make contact with those outside their circle. Unless it's on Facebook. People don't even care if strangers like their stupid ass posts. But not my sparkling clean cupcake date. He's a little freshly starched dream! I give him a wave as I drive off.

I am back in my car, driving and I swear, I don't remember even starting the car. I'm starting to feel lost. So lost. Not as in the "I have lost who I used to be, and I need to find myself" lost, like John throws at me daily. I feel lost in my head. I am going to these places, buying these things, yet there is a milky film covering everything. Nothing is exactly clear and I feel like I'm not the one making the choices here. I swear to you, I just passed Paris Hilton again, in front of a Gelson's market. Paris must be stalking me.

I just don't feel in control anymore. It starts to make me nervous, this out of control feeling, so I pull over. I grip the steering wheel and just breathe for a few minutes. Not sure how long. Everything flashes before me. My life. My marriage. The choices I've made. My children. I think I'm dying. I'm pretty sure these "life flashes" happen right before you die. My heart is in my throat. Sweat is pouring off me. So this is it? This is how I die? Cupcake crumbs on my face and a car full of packages, stuff I'll never get to use? Dead in my mom van on Santa Monica Boulevard? Really? This what I've lived for? This is my big legacy?

I'm not sure, but I think I do die, at least for a couple of minutes. But, God being the good and wonderful God that he is, doesn't let me just slip away in a minivan with a gut full of cupcakes. He brings me back to life just in time to see the parking meter cop park in front of me. I roll down my window, "Just leaving!" I wave and start my car.

I keep driving. The window open, wind on my face. The air feels good, even though it is thick, smoggy, cut with a knife L.A. air, it is nice to feel it blowing on my face. Oddly, it is also nice to smell exhaust, street pavement, and even cigarette smoke. (I HATE smelling cigarette smoke usually, and cough and sputter at people who smoke just to make them feel bad.) However, considering I just died for a few minutes, everything smells great right now.

It seems like I've been driving for a long time now. However, in Los Angeles, time on the road can be deceiving. One day you can be in your car for thirty minutes and go from Pasadena to the Ocean. Other days, you can be in your car for thirty minutes and may have only gone 2 miles. You think you have short cuts, that you have this town mastered and THAT is the day this town smacks you upside the head and says "Not today bitch!" I start trying to pay attention to the street names and just can't quite seem to catch any. I try to turn on my navigation system in the car, but sometimes Wanda is very fickle. (Yes, we named our navigation system Wanda because she has a female voice.) We try to be nice to her, give her compliments so she'll always work for us, but she hates me. She's always liked John and worked for him, but Wanda has always thought of me as the "other woman" so of COURSE on this day when I really need her, she zooms out to a world map view and has a pinpoint in Nicaragua. Huh?

I keep driving. The temperature seems to have gotten even cooler. And is that fog? It's difficult to understand that there is ever fog in Los Angeles, because we just always assume that it's smog. (Beverly Hills people call it "haze".) But I think this actually may be fog. I have NO idea where I am. At this point, I don't even know how long I've been driving. The clock on the car says 8:00 p.m. which I know can't be right, as it's still day time. My cell phone says 1:00 p.m. That's a pretty big discrepancy. I push the navigation button again to see if I can get Wanda to "guide me home", but now she is showing some location in Calgary. What is she doing to me? Yes, I've lived in Los Angeles my whole life, but ever since these navigation systems have come along, I've just stopped paying attention. I have no CLUE where I am. I try to look for the San Gabriel mountains, that's always how I get my "north/south" bearings in L.A. when I get lost, but with the fog, I can't see them. This is really weird!

Completely lost in the city I've grown up in. What a strange feeling.

I drive further and further hoping to see some landmark, a hotel, a restaurant, a street, anything that will tell me where I am. Nothing. I don't recognize one thing! How bizarre. If someone held a knife to me and forced me to guess, I'd say I was somewhere east of Downtown? Strangely, I'm not scared, I just feel weird that I have no clue where I am. I'm sure eventually I will see something that I recognize. I decide to park, go to the bathroom and just ask someone. I have to turn down several side streets in order to find a parking spot. I try to see the parking signs to see if I have to put money in the meter, but oddly, there is no meter. No parking meter in Los Angeles? Okaaaaaaaaay. I start walking, there is NO one on this street. I turn down another street.

Here is where I need to tell you something peculiar about me. Many, MANY times I will view my life like I'm watching a movie. Everything is shot from my point of view. Complete with special effects. As I turn the corner and look into the street it happens. I cannot control this phenomenon. It just happens. Everything is in slow motion, even me. My head slowly scans this narrow street. Through the fog I can see some stores and a few people in the distance milling around. All in slow, sluggish motion. I see some Asian writing on the store signs and some paper lanterns hanging outside of the shops. The lanterns blow so very slowly in the nonexistent wind. There are chimes too, gently dinging together. Maybe the fog is moving them, because clearly, there is NO wind. The fog IS moving, slowly across the businesses and people, only giving me glimpses of what is there. The minute I focus on something and almost understand what I'm looking at, the fog envelopes it. It's very calm here, not scary. Not a lot of noise either. Just the chimes. I don't hear any talking, cars, or the usual sounds coming from businesses. My best guess would be that I made it to Chinatown, but I've been to Chinatown many times. This just doesn't look like any street I've ever been on. If I am in Chinatown, I'm only about 15 minutes from home. I can just ask someone.

I start to walk down the foggy street with paper lanterns blowing in the mysterious non-wind. However, the movie vision is still in effect and I'm walking in slow motion. I don't want to walk fast though. Don't want to spoil the quietness and stillness of this street. I don't think anyone has looked at me yet, can't quite tell. I keep trying to make eye contact, but the fog is preventing me from doing so. I keep walking, passing eyeless, silent people for about twenty minutes until I am drawn into a store. I hadn't see the store from the street, but somehow find my way inside. There are no windows and I can't see the street from where I am. I feel like I am downstairs in the store. I am completely startled and jump out of my skin when someone speaks to me.

Shop owner: "Hello."

Suddenly the movie has stopped playing and things are back to normal speed. I turn to assess who has spoken to me. Wow…the fog fades all around me. Everything is clear, including the small Asian man with long white hair who stands before me. I can't stop looking around his store and then back to him. Around the store and back at him. Unbelievable! I am IN the movie Gremlins. I am in the store in Chinatown where the dad buys the gremlin for his son for Christmas. I wouldn't have known, except I just watched that movie with Andrew a few months ago. I have to ask.

Me: "I'm sorry, was Gremlins filmed here? Were you in the movie Gremlins?"

Oh, I really regret that question the minute I see his confused face.

Shop Owner: "Gremlins?"

Me: "I'm sorry, forget that. Nothing. Hello, I…um…appear to be lost. Can you tell me, am I in Chinatown?"

Shop Owner: "You are lost? Not any more. You are here."

Me: "Oh thank you, I was just wondering…"

The small Asian man cuts me off.

Shop Owner: "Please, won't you have a look around? There may be something to your liking."

So odd, suddenly I didn't care about where I was, I knew I'd get home just fine and that this sweet little old gentleman would help me. I just started shopping. After all, that is what I set out to do today, SHOP! I look around. I swear, it REALLY does look like the store in the beginning of Gremlins. How odd. I don't see any Mogwai, so I guess that's a good thing, because that would just really freak me out!

There are frogs, and Buddhas, and chimes, and silk, and fans, and bamboo and everything you'd expect to see from a store in Chinatown. Clearly that must be where I am. The old fellow is suddenly back in front of me with a cup of hot tea. Ahhhh, that looks wonderful. He hands it to me and motions for me to sit. I turn around and see a sofa, or maybe it's a love seat. A bit smaller than a sofa. Funny, I hadn't seen that love seat a minute ago. I sit on it and take a sip of tea. Here's where I snap back into a movie. Not only do I feel, but I see the weight of the world fall off of me. It seeps off my shoulders down onto the ground. Like I was made of wax and am melting. The hatred for John, the stress of impending divorce, the confusion of my day, everything. Just melts away. I sip more tea and concentrate on this wonderful feeling I am experiencing. I am surprised to see the bottom of my cup so soon and look up to see the small Asian man looking at me, smiling.

Me: "I'm sorry, this is…this tea, it's very good, thank you."

Shop Owner: "My name is Tian."

Me: "Hello Tian, my name is Denise."

He smiles and nods, more like a sitting bow. I really like bowing. I think it's such a lovely sign of respect and a happy greeting. I think we should all bow in the United States. Would probably be less crime. It just starts a conversation off right, when two people bow. I have actually bowed myself, just involuntarily sometimes, when I'm speaking to someone. Wonderful tradition, I vote YES on bowing! Tian is just watching me have all these thoughts in my head, smiling and nodding, like I'm speaking out loud. Weird.

Tian: "Hello Denise. You are happy now?"

Tian speaks so slow, and the sound of his voice is like a musical instrument. So lulling. I don't feel like I should speak right away when he finishes speaking. I have to let his last note resonate in the air before I speak.

Me: "Well, I do feel much better, that's for sure. Thank you for this tea. What kind is it? It's so relaxing."

Tian: "A special blend. A touch of happiness and a touch of clarity."

Me: "Oh, clarity and happiness. That is exactly what I needed. Perfect."

I just sit there, and look at this man. I feel so close to him. Like I love him. Like he's my sweet Uncle George that I've bonded with my whole life. I just feel love from him, like he truly cares about me. This sure is the strangest day I have ever had in my entire life.

I think of John, and just adding to the bizarreness going on inside my head, I actually feel sorry for him. Several scenes play in my head at once, like the TV's that allow you to have multiple channels playing at the same time. Several little squares within your TV playing different channels. I select one square to play and it becomes larger than the other squares. It begins to play the scene when John was making fajitas one night. He was using a small chopper we had, I think we got it from Bed Bath & Beyond. I HATED that chopper and had been meaning to throw it away. Of COURSE John goes and gets that chopper. I was sure he was using the chopper just to piss me off. That thing is so difficult to clean that I've cut myself every single time I've ever washed it. I knew he had done that on purpose, to annoy me, because John never washes anything and knew I would be the one washing it and KNEW how angry I'd get having to wash that chopper. He also KNEW that I always cut myself on that thing, so in reality, he wanted me to cut myself. I remember thinking at the time, he probably wished I'd slice open an artery, right there, at the kitchen sink and just drop to the ground with the chopper in hand and die. But, he didn't get his wish. He was in the middle of chopping a green pepper and I yanked the chopper from his hand, marched outside, and threw it in the trashcan. He was so pissed at me. He threw everything he had chopped for the fajitas into the garbage and went and got into bed. I told the kids to make peanut butter and jelly sandwiches and I got into the shower.

But now, sitting here, in this store, with Tian, at this moment, suddenly I see John's side. How odd. He was just trying to help out by making dinner. It really wasn't a conspiracy to slice open my arteries. He was just trying to chop a pepper. Wow. It seems so silly right now. Maybe it's the tea. I look up to see Tian still smiling at me, except now he has a pot of the steaming tea.

Me: "Oh, yes thank you, it's just wonderful tea."

Tian: "Special tea, my grandmother's recipe."

I smiled, take another sip of tea and then see all the squares playing in my head again. I select one square where I am sitting at the computer, looking at John's Facebook page. I remember getting so angry at him because he had reconnected with an old mutual friend of ours from college and was having a conversation back and forth with him and NEVER mentioned me. I had accused John of being embarrassed by me and not wanting to say he was married to me. John had put up some pictures of him and the kids…WITHOUT me in them!

I had told him that he was already divorced in his head, mentally living without me. Not even trying. He started off with the "you're crazy, too sensitive, reading into things" and that just drives me INSANE when he does that. John knows that too. Anytime he starts that "you're crazy" stuff on me, it's going to go bad. During our whole marriage together, I've told him I hate when he does that. That it makes me feel like the wife in *Gaslight* an old Ingrid Bergman movie, where her husband tries to make her think she's going insane. John will look at me with that bewildered look on his face, like I am speaking in tongues, when in fact, I'm speaking very clear, very plain English.

He just kept protesting, that I was getting too "worked up" about it. Of course, we all know, when someone tells you that you are getting "worked up" about something, THEY'RE the one who is trying to hide something. So I sort of forced him to put a picture of me on his Facebook, but it only made things worse. His friends never commented on my picture. That made me feel horrible. Facebook is so great when people love you and you get all the comments and attention, but when your husband never mentions that he is married, or posts a picture of you and no one comments or likes it, it can be truly depressing. So…I got mad because no one liked my photo on Facebook. Hmmm. That seems… so stupid. I look up and see Tian smiling at me.

Me: "Tian, are you married?"

Tian: "Oh yes, for fifty-two years."

I choke on my tea for a second. NO ONE in Los Angeles has been married for fifty-two years. You make it to ten years and you are considered old and boring. Celebrities only make it to two years.

Me: "Fifty-two? Wow, that's amazing. And you're still in love?"

Tian smiles at me, for what seems like about five minutes before he speaks.

Tian: "My wife is Shuang. Her name means an open heart. Not one corner of your heart can be closed if you are to remain married. When you start closing doors to your heart that is the day your marriage begins to fail. Your heart Denise, is completely closed."

My mouth drops open. I can't help it. It's true. My heart has been closed, shut tight for years. Boarded up. Cobwebs. And this tiny Asian man can see that.

Tian: "When we first married, it was an immature love. The love of the beginning. The love of excitement. The love grew and matured and aged with every passing year. We both held onto it, letting love mold us, working with love, not fighting it. Not trying to hold onto the immature love. Embracing each distinct love that came with the passing years. The love of today is different than the love of yesterday. But the love of today, is much stronger and deeper than the original love. It has bound us together for life. Nothing can break the love we share today. It is impossible once you have passed to the final stages of love. Shuang and I will be together always, if we are in this world, or in another. There is comfort and joy in knowing we can never be broken."

I am crying. There are actually tears running down my cheeks. I don't even understand why I'm crying or what is going on, I just know I feel so sad. An hour ago, I hated John with every ounce of me, and now, I'm sitting on a love seat, crying about the love I didn't take care of. I am so overwhelmed. That's probably it. I'm just tired and I'm getting emotional. But I have to admit, there is something here. There is a feeling I haven't had in years. It's so strange that this feeling is inside me. It's so foreign to feel this. I believe the feeling is "hope", but I'm not sure, as it's been so long.

I am so confused. I wipe the tears from my cheeks and Tian continues.

Tian: "We were given a gift. Our love. It is up to us to protect it. Each person has duties and responsibilities to guard and nurture the love. Like a garden. If you expect someone else to water it, the garden will die. If you wait for your partner to prune and fertilize the garden, you have walked away from many fruits. If you let the snails and birds eat your fruit, you have failed to protect your garden. It is a daily job to be taken very seriously. If you work in your garden every day, your garden can sustain you. It can feed you and keep you content. When two people completely ignore their garden, the garden will surely die. When love dies inside you, it is one of the most hopeless feelings in the world. So many things we can cope with, if we have love. But when love is gone, the world becomes darker. It becomes more difficult to confront daily ups and downs. The world becomes colder without an open heart."

I just sit there. I'm so numb. So not in touch with my body right now. For all I know, I could be dreaming. What if I'm sleeping? What if I'm actually happily married and this is all a dream? The shopping, this day...and Tian. All a dream. I would give anything to wake up right now, be happily married and forget all of this. I am really tired of being unhappy.

Tian speaks again, and I realize I'm still here. No dream. No such luck.

Tian: "Perhaps you want to take another look around before you leave? Perhaps you will see something you need?"

I don't want to be rude, Tian has been so sweet to me, so I tell him "sure" and take the last sip of my tea. I can't really tell you what happened after that. Considering I feel like I have spent most of this day in a fog, I guess it's not surprising. My mind just isn't itself. I just haven't been able to focus today. My mind just keeps spinning, thinking of things. Strangely, I start thinking of happy things. Memories from the past, when John and I were so happy together. I know it may be difficult for you to believe, but we really did used to be completely, over the top in love.

I remember once when we went to the Madonna Inn in San Luis Obispo. We thought it was going to be so cool. The pictures on the website looked incredible. Such a unique hotel, every room is different, crazy, weird, bizarre. Drove straight from Los Angeles, didn't stop once. We had fun and romance on the brain, and not even food lured us off the freeway. Well, the Madonna Inn, truthfully, is complete insanity. Horrific might be a good word. We were so scared. We ended up only spending one night, and getting up and checking out by 8:00 a.m. because we were so freaked out by the place.

Our room had two king sized beds, foot to foot. That kept creeping us out, like there was supposed to be another couple in there with us. Swingers or something. We felt all gross in the beds, like what had gone on there, in that room before us? In these two king sized beds? We were sure that the sheets weren't completely clean. We were afraid to put our legs completely straight down in the bed, sure that our toes would find a big hair ball or something worse.

The fireplace took up the whole wall, it was this huge stone sculpture and it was extremely creepy. Honestly, there is nothing cool about the Madonna Inn. It's a Texas Chain Saw Massacre, Freddie Krueger waiting in the bathroom kind of a place. John went to get some ice and was confronted by a total biker dude, in chaps and a leather vest, straight out of a Rob Zombie movie, tattoos everywhere, telling him we could come back to his room for cocktails. Uh huh. Yeah, like we were going to do that. And have our throats slit, at the Madonna Inn? Gee, no thank you, but really, how generous of you to extend such a gracious invitation!

We didn't sleep well. We certainly didn't have any "fun". We just held each other, looking forward to when we could get the hell out of there. It was one of the strangest, scariest nights of our lives, but how we laughed about it the next day. We couldn't stop laughing about it. I always told John we should have gone and partied with the Rob Zombie guy. I could have been impregnated by him, and our baby could be Spike, instead of our boring Andrew. Once we were safely away from the Madonna Inn, and our throats were still intact, it turned into one of the funniest nights of our lives. From that point on, every time we checked into a hotel room, John would always say "Well, this room is nice, but it could really use another king sized bed." That one night gave us so much material. Made us laugh for many years.

John and I had so many times like that. Experiences that completely bonded us together, we thought for life. Times that were funny only to us. Memories that only we had and shared, that we could bring up years later, and laugh till we cried over them. It's really difficult to believe that we have deteriorated into what we are. That I hate everything about him. The way he eats. Walks. How he moves his toes when he sleeps. Taps his thumbs on the steering wheel when he drives. His handwriting. I even hate how he breathes! What kind of insanity is that? I can't even stand to be around the man I married because his breathing drives me batty! He makes a sound in his nostrils when he breathes in and the air rushing past his nose hairs makes them wiggle. And the pores in his nose are oddly large or something. And his nose is always moist, sweating, especially when he eats. Dear God, how does this happen?

I think of the time we rode a pedicab (those little cart things you pedal around by the beach) onto the 101 Freeway. Oh yes we did! Everyone always argues with me when I tell them this story, but being that I had a moment of clarity during those crazed moments on the 101 freeway, I took a picture. It shows John trying to maneuver the pedicab on the freeway, with a big rig whizzing by in the background. Now, we weren't complete morons (50% moron maybe, but not complete), we didn't just get on an on-ramp and pedal onto the freeway. It was during a time of freeway construction on the 101 through Santa Barbara in the 90's. Yes, you were only supposed to pedal your little cart along the ocean, but we wanted to get to State Street where the good shopping was. We did a series of turns and easily turned left onto the freeway. We always blamed it on the city of Santa Barbara, for not marking the freeway entrance well enough. Surely we cannot be the only people who drove a pedicab onto the 101 freeway during that time! ? OK, well, maybe we were, and I guess that makes the story that much more amazing. At first, when we saw the cars zooming by us, we laughed, thought it was hysterical that this was happening to us. But soon we were peddling for our lives, with people honking at us, and John had to lift the pedicab over a divider to get us off the freeway, it really wasn't so funny. We definitely stopped laughing and started sweating. It was a total panic moment, him finding the strength to lift that thing. Cars were flying by so close and I was just sure someone was going to swerve a little to the right and clip us. We would have been complete and utter toast.

For a while after that experience, we just felt like idiots. Who gets stuck on the 101 Freeway in a surrey? But after a few years, it was one of John's favorite stories to tell. He'd let it go on for a while, with people not believing, thinking he was just a big exaggerator. Then he'd pull out the photo. John would laugh and laugh at people's reactions. "No we weren't drinking," he'd tell them. He thought that was so funny. Like surely for someone to pedal a pedicab onto a freeway, you must have been drinking. But nope, not us. We just wanted to get to State Street.

The worst part was, you aren't supposed to have those carts on State Street. There are lots of people walking and shopping on that street, so once we got there, a police officer told us we had to turn around. We headed back to the pedicab rental place. No one wanted us on State Street. Everyone was so mad at us! We never even got to shop! We paid our hourly pedicab rental fee for a crazy, high anxiety pedal trip that we'd never, ever forget.

The memories were just playing in my head. Like old movies. We didn't even own one of those old projectors, we've had regular video cameras our whole marriage. But in my head, all of our old, happy memories were playing on the kind of set up my granddaddy used to have. A projector set up on the kitchen table, with a screen that pulled up and hooked on top. I kept seeing the memories of John and I, and laughing to myself. It felt so unsettling to be having these happy memories of John. The best memories. The kind that warmed your heart and gave you a new zest for life. It went on for hours.

I think I must have drifted off. I wake up, in the minivan, in front of my house. I have no memory of leaving Tian's store, or driving home. Um, that seems pretty dangerous. I drove? Without knowing what I was doing?   Although that's how everyone in Los Angeles gets from one place to another. You pretty much have to place yourself into a hypnotic trance in order to deal with the constant traffic and assholes in this town. Weird. I look at the clock, 1:10 a.m. Wow, one o'clock in the morning? My concept of time was completely skewed today, but one in the morning? I am just shocked that I've been out all day and into the morning. I'm not sure what time I was at Tian's store in Chinatown, but I would figure it was sometime around three or four o'clock in the afternoon. So what have I been doing for the last nine hours??? I grab some packages and it doesn't even make a dent in the amount of packages in the car. It will take several trips.

As I walk through the front door, I drop my packages. My jaw also drops. John is there, looking at me with more hate than I've ever seen in him, ever. But it's not John I'm looking at.

The living room is completely filled with bags, boxes and new furniture items. My god, I bought all this? Filled. Absolutely filled to the brink. I see that the packages are spilling into the dining room and can even get a glimpse of more boxes and bags in the family room. I can't possibly have purchased all this, could I? Although, it's true, I can't account for nine hours. Maybe I had a blackout, like an alcoholic, except this was a "shop-a-holic blackout". Is there such a thing? I'm guessing so, since our house is completely packed to the gills with things I purchased today. It had to be me. I did this. I am completely dumbfounded at the amount of things that are in this house. I really did it. I really stuck it to John. This is what he gets. You neglect your wife, you make her miserable, this is what you get.

I look at John finally. His face is a combination of sadness and rage. I stay strong in my decision and gave him a "Yeah, what are you going to do about it" face, raising my eyebrows slightly. I can tell, I've done the one thing that would hurt John the most. He's worked so hard for his pristine credit, this is a huge blow to him. He looks beyond anger. I think I see disappointment on his face, but I look away. I don't want to see disappointment, I only want him to be angry. He turns and walks upstairs.

I finally take a step and begin to survey the bags, boxes and new furniture in our home. I can barely make my way through the room. I don't even recognize most of this stuff. I have absolutely zero memory of buying most of these things. How bizarre. I really did slip into some sort of blackout. That seems mighty dangerous to be out in the world, charging on credit cards during a blackout. Thank goodness that's what I *wanted* to do, otherwise, this could have been a disaster.

I notice the television is on. One of those late night music video channels. How amusing that "Tainted Love" is playing. Even our TV knows the sorry state of our marriage.

Once I ran to you, now I run from you…

Story of my life, right there, in that little sentence. Completely sums up how I feel about John. I start looking through packages on an area on the sofa, sifting through bags that hold new towels, sheets, candles, candleholders, a small lamp, new dishes, and a few coats. I move the bags aside to make a place to sit down. WHAT? I drop a bag with plates in it, and I hear them break as they hit another bag with something hard in it. But, I definitely don't care. I am frozen with an odd tingling sensation, like prickly heat, but cold. There goes my jaw again, open, hanging there. I've experienced a heck of a lot of jaw dropping today. I notice my hand shaking as it reaches out to touch the sofa. The love seat! The one I sat on in Tian's store! What is going on here? I am so confused. So tired and a bit freaked out. Did I buy this? I must have.

I sit on the love seat and survey the room. Now the television is playing another interesting video. I think the TV is taunting me. "Poison Arrow" by ABC.

Who broke my heart, you did, you did.

Bow to the target,

Blame Cuipid, Cupid.

You think you're smart

Stupid, stupid.

OK, the TV is starting to freak me out a little.

Or is it just so obvious that EVERYONE and EVERYTHING in the world knows about our failed relationship. Suddenly I feel warm. And relaxed. And slightly positive. Positive because I have truly stung

John? Hit him below the belt? Maybe…I'm not exactly feeling proud as I look across all the packages and boxes. Actually, I'd say I'm starting to feel slightly nauseous. I've had a rough day. Revenge is extremely hard work. I pull over a bag with towels in it and lay my head on it. I put my feet up on a box on the edge of the love seat. I'll just take a second and relax. Something I haven't done all day. Something I haven't done for weeks. As I drift off, I hear the TV playing "Holding Back the Years" by Simply Red:

Chance for me to escape from all I know.
Holding back the tears.
There's nothing here has grown.
I've wasted all my tears,
Wasted all those years.
Nothing has the chance to be good…

My head keeps thinking for a minute after my eyes are closed tight. Yes, wasted many tears and many years. Simply Red, so true, so true.

John, December 19th 1:30 a.m.

I could scream and rage at her but the kids would hear. That would suck. So her plan was to ruin my credit. Obviously charge to the limit, probably over the limit on all our credit cards. Great plan I guess, if you're looking to really hurt me. So amazing to me that her goal was to hurt me. A conscious effort to cause me pain. She knew how deeply that would hurt me.

My credit used to be horrible. After I got out of college, I just did myself in. Wouldn't pay the cable bill, then just switch to another cable company. I got credit cards, and never had any intention of paying anything on them. I'd charge them to the max, and never make ONE payment. I had some of my credit cards confiscated at stores as the credit card company called them in. I was completely irresponsible. After becoming an adult and mulling that over, I believe it was a result of my upbringing. I was pretty sheltered and not given responsibility. No one taught me to be responsible. No one explained to me managing money. My mom liked to keep me dependent on her, so she just paid for everything. It really didn't do me any favors. You think someone loves you because they are paying for things and buying you things. But often, all that showering with gifts can come from a very insidious place. It did in my case. It was all meant to keep me under my mother's control.

Getting out, growing up and becoming independent was a long and meaningful process for me. It meant cutting the ties that were so tightly bound with my mother. It meant owning myself and my actions. It meant paying all my bad debts and taking financial responsibility for myself, for the first time in my life. So for Denise to pull this, is truly low of her. She's the only person on this earth that knows how damaging this would be to me. There is the woman I loved. Going out and purposely doing something that she knew would be devastating to me. On my salary, I will barely be able to make minimum payments on all that stuff. Truly amazing what has become of us.

I told you she was different from the woman I married. THAT Denise would have never done anything intentional to hurt me. Ever. All I can do is look forward to a time when Denise is no longer in my life.

Denise, December 19th 7:00 a.m.

Not the most comfortable thing in the world to wake up with your face on a plastic shopping bag and your legs on a Crate & Barrel box. Something incredibly sharp is sticking into my ribs. I move a bit so I can reach whatever is protruding into my side. Lovely. It's a silver pasta spoon, with those spiky things on it to grab the pasta. I look at my side, and there are spike marks in it. I peer into the bag my head was on. I really do like these towels. Very pretty. black & white. They don't really match anything though. Andrew walks through the room, doesn't even look at me. Doesn't even notice all the bags and boxes for that matter. Just walks straight through to the kitchen.

God, I do feel like the world's worst mother. But look, I am going through hell right now. At least I'm still alive for my kids. I didn't kill myself. I figure, when I get this whole thing sorted out, and John and I are divorced and living our separate lives, THEN I can be a mother again. I'm taking a little personal time for me to work through this. I will bake cookies and read stories once again. I promise. Right now I am losing my husband. Losing my husband? Wow. That just doesn't sound right. I'm not sure. I don't think I want to lose my husband. My husband? Suddenly all the words I'm thinking sound SO bizarre. The word "husband" doesn't sound right. Hus-band. Huzz-ban. Huzz. Does that ever happen to you? You start saying a word and then suddenly the spelling of that word sounds all wrong? It happened to me once in elementary school. I forgot how to spell "of". I remembered that "oven" is spelled with an "ov" so it made sense that "of" was spelled "ov". I went back and forth in my head for an over an hour on that one. Who spells "of" with an F? Should've been a V! It's so obvious! Everybody knows. Everyone laughs at the "f" in of.

So back to my head. I feel strange. Maybe it's just because I've been lying on packages all night. I feel good. I feel…positive? How weird. What do I have to be positive about? My eyes slowly move across all the packages and boxes to look at the TV. The music television station is still on, but oddly, it's playing "Never Tear Us Apart" by INXS.

I was standing
You were there.
Two worlds collided
And they could never tear us apart…

Strange. I guess the TV doesn't know what's going on with John or it wouldn't be playing THAT song. The day we brought Amber home from the hospital that song played in the car. John had turned around to look at Amber in her car seat, then looked at me with tears in his eyes. It was a great moment. I felt such a deep love with him. Funny how a song can bring back actual feelings from a certain time in your life. Why am I even saying this? First, like the TV knows my life! And second, why am I thinking about a happy moment with John? BIZARRE! I'm freaking myself out.

Suddenly, in all my thoughts and music, John walks into the room. I smile at him. WHAT? What the hell am I doing? It isn't a mean smile, like, "Look at all this shit you're going to have to pay for", it's a "Good morning, how are you" smile! I have completely lost it! John, thankfully, just looks at me and walks into the kitchen. I hear him talking with Andrew. There is definitely something wrong with me. I can't control myself. I need to go take a shower.

Andrew, December 19th 7:15 a.m.

There is something different today from the usual fighting and screaming that my parents do. First, when I woke up, the house was totally full of packages and boxes and bags from stores. Obviously my mom's latest plan to stick it to my dad. Pretty mean if you ask me. There goes our college money. Pretty selfish too. She buys all this crap, just for revenge? She really spent her time doing that? OK. I guess it worked too, because my dad looks pretty bad today. It's weird, they aren't even yelling at each other, which would be the normal event after one of them goes off and does something stupid like this. But, no yelling. The house actually seems very calm and still.

Maybe they've just had enough, like the rest of us. Maybe they're just tired, over it and ready to move on. I'd love to have my parents back. I actually miss them during the day-to-day living. I haven't told anyone about my days at school for a very long time. I listen to Molly and Amber, cause I figure they need someone to talk to. But I've been pretty lonely.

Parents really don't think about kids during this whole divorce thing. I mean, they think they do. But they don't really sit down, and get in touch with what we're feeling. They have gone through years of misery, thinking they were doing something for us. Staying together…for the kids. How completely dumb. What they've done for us is take both parents away. Our mom and dad haven't been there for us for years. We've pretty much just done everything ourselves. It's either going to make us stronger adults, or really cold adults, unable to have relationships of our own. One thing is for sure, the LAST thing I want is to have a marriage like my parents have.

I'd leave way before it got to the point my parents are. I'd never do that to my kids. And, I'd talk to my kids. I'd involve them in decisions. I'd have discussions with them about what's going on. My parents just argue, then they each go to a different part of the house to mope, and it's up to us to do homework, bathe, make dinner. It's ridiculous. Like all their arguing has given them permission to not parent anymore. I don't think they have any idea what they are doing to us. I can't believe they'd continue like this if they knew.

Well, have to make sure the girls are ready for school. One more day and we're on holiday break. Thank God!

Denise, December 19th 8:42 a.m.

I've had a shower, and yes, I do feel more like me, if you were wondering. And I know you were. It's really strange typing out my thoughts every day, like I'm talking to someone. But I guess I am talking to myself. Keeping a diary or journal just makes me feel even more lonely. Like I have to talk to myself because I don't have a husband. Partner. Best friend. Hmmm. Bizarre. Probably is doing me some good though. At least I'm getting out all my thoughts, and that's better than keeping them all inside. Right?

I've seen John writing too, but I guess he's changed the password on his computer, because I can't log on anymore. The password used to be "lover123". Now it's probably "imadick321". Or, "asshole007". But I tried those, and they didn't work. No, it's probably "wifesabitch01". I should remember to try that one. I wouldn't be surprised.

Definitely a shower is what I needed because now I feel like myself again, filled with a nice fresh batch of hate towards that man, if you want to call him a man. If only John had climbed into his parents experimental

83

weather balloon as a child, and sailed off. Freezing to death, limb by limb. Spinning out of control, looking like frozen armless cauliflower until he hit the ground in his jiffy pop death trap. But no such luck. He grew up into the ultimate dick. We're talking Charlie Sheen dick level. He just doesn't care about anyone but himself.

I think a lot of husbands are like this. They expect the world from their wives. Do my laundry. Clean up after me. Take care of me when I'm sick, because I become a total and complete baby. (Sidenote about what a baby John is. Do you know what he does EVERY SINGLE time he hits himself anywhere on his body? He might smack his hand on the door. Or bump his head on a cabinet. Whatever. The very next thing he does is wipe a hand across whatever part of his body that got hit, then look at the hand to see if there's any blood. THEN, he keeps doing that. Thinking maybe there will be delayed bleeding or something. SUCH a baby!!!)

They think because they have a job (hopefully) and go to work, that's it. That's all they're responsible for. They don't have to help with kids, or making dinner, or laundry, or picking up tons of crap off the carpet or ANYthing! THEN, on top of that, they expect us to do all our work AND theirs, and then be some bedroom goddess all hot & bothered and ready for lovin'. Then they complain they get no action! Pisses me off beyond belief. I'm on the verge of hyperventilating just thinking about the unfairness of it all.

I think perhaps the only way to truly be happy with a man is to never have kids and marry a man who has family money and doesn't have to work. Like say, a prince or a king. Hmmm. Thinking of Prince Charles, this probably wouldn't work either. He seems like a big dick too. I mean, if Princess Di (god rest her soul) had to get rid of him, I probably would have too.

I walk back downstairs with my renewed hatred for John. It feels good. How I am supposed to feel. Comfortable. I've hated him for so long, it just feels right. Then, I see him. Sitting on my new love seat! Granted, it is a piece of furniture I didn't even know I bought, but still. What kind of nerve is that? You don't go and sit on something that I bought to make you miserable. WTF!

I march myself right over to the other side of the love seat, shove a bunch of bags off onto the floor, and plop down. I give him one of my special up and down looks of disgust. Only problem is when I looked down to his feet, I could feel myself make a hideous triple chin. I quickly looked up and straightened my posture...to which...he smiles. Actually, he chuckles. It takes me so off guard, that I too chuckle. What. Is. Going. On!!!!!!!!!!!!!!!!!!!!!!!!!!!!!!!

I'm sitting there on the sofa, chuckling with John. Really, I think someone is putting crack in my coffee because I am not feeling right. Then John starts the strangest conversation with me.

John: "Pretty crazy place we've gotten ourselves to, huh?"

I stare at him a very long time before I speak. I'm not exactly sure what's going on. I glance at the television, still playing 80's music. "With or Without You" by U2. I squint at the TV, I swear it's alive. John looks almost…friendly. Surely this is some sort of trap that will be brought up in divorce court against me. Finally I answer.

Me: "Yeah, crazy."

John: "Have any idea how we get ourselves out?"

What is he up to? My head is spinning. This has to be a trap. He's going to try to get me to admit about sleeping with the neighbor, or the paperboy, which of course didn't happen, but I still feel like I'm being framed.

Suddenly, as if someone turned the channel on the television, I find myself thinking of a Halloween, probably about 8 years ago. John loves to try and make food look like it does in magazines. We saw this really cool photo spread of Halloween spooky delicacies. I like to think it was in Martha Stewart, but it was probably in Good Housekeeping. Anyway, it was basically red pasta that looked like it was bloody pasta. I know, that doesn't sound wonderful, but in the magazine, of course it looked amazing. So John decided to make this for a party we were going to. Have you ever brought a dish to a party that NO one ate? Where everything on the table around it was decreasing in size and your dish was sitting there, untouched? I have to admit, I didn't even have any. He used so much red food coloring, the white dish turned red. Ruined the dish. The pasta was just sitting in red juice, and it wasn't marinara. It totally looked like a lab experiment gone wrong. Way wrong. No one would touch it. Oh, people ooohed and ahhhhhed over it, laughing, pointing, saying how "festive" it looked, but in the end, no one gutted even one bite down. It looked repulsive. It looked like a bowl of veins. We laughed so hard in the car on the way home, with our full bowl of veins that no one touched. We got home and took pictures of each other with the veins. I love how embarrassing, ridiculous moments turn into such great memories.

At that moment I chuckle out loud and snap back into reality. The TV turns back to the twenty-four hour a day John channel. It completely surprises me to be sitting on the love seat with John. I have to look around a moment to realize where I am. John is sitting there smiling at me.

Me: "What?"

John is still smiling.

John: "Nothing."

Me: "What? Why are you smiling?"

John takes a moment to answer.

John: "I was just thinking about the time I made that bloody spaghetti for that Halloween party that time."

I stood up. It was some sort of immediate knee-jerk reaction. I am shocked into standing. I look at him, for half a second, no, maybe an 1/8 of a second, I ALMOST want to hug him. But as I stand, I feel the blood rushing back into my head, making my thoughts normal. Filling me with the hatred that belongs here.

Me: "I don't remember that."

I turn and walk upstairs. The warm person in me feels a little bad. To shoot him down like that. Like, why couldn't I just sit there and have a moment with him? A happy moment?

Why do things have to be so hateful and spiteful all the time? Why can't we be that couple that gets divorced and stays friends? That still goes out to dinner? Because I know that's not what I want. I want to hate John forever. That "sweet John" was the man I married. He was the man I fell in love with. But the "self-centered John" is the man I'm now married to. The man that works late at the office on my birthday when he doesn't have to. The man that would rather go fishing with his friends than do anything with me. The man that used to go grocery shopping with me all the time, but turned into the man that expected it and was "disappointed" in me when I forgot to get everything we needed. The man that turns on the television as a means of not having to listen to anything I say. The man that used to be so romantic, couldn't get enough of me, turned into the man who couldn't stand to look at me. Who made me self-conscious about my stretch marks. He turned into a man that made me feel ugly. I hate John, and I can't ever forget that.

John, December 19th 1:04 p.m.

The most bizarre thing happened this morning. Actually, it was a bizarre feeling. It was the tiniest glimmer of the feeling I used to have with Denise. The old Denise. Why? Why would that happen, today of all days? When she has done something so mean and cruel to me? I am a little confused as to why I felt that today. It didn't last very long, but it was there. It was strong. I remembered that feeling and it felt very good. But why? I will definitely bring this up to my therapist, at the risk of sounding insane. All I've done is spew my hatred for Denise in session after session. Now I'm going to go in and say, "Hey doc, so I was sitting on this love seat that my wife bought in an attempt to charge the credit cards to their limits...surrounded by hundreds of packages that she bought just to hurt me, and I felt the old spark for Denise." That sounds totally nuts, doesn't it?

Maybe I should just forget that ever happened. Not bring it up. It's not like Denise is going to change. She didn't even remember my bloody vein pasta. I think she's forgotten about all the great times we used to have. Blocked them out so she can hate me more. I guess it's easier to hate someone when you don't ever remember loving them.

Denise, December 19th 12:00 Noon

I'm sitting here at the computer, thinking about what I wrote this morning. About John planning to accusing me of sleeping with the paperboy. Considering the paperboy is 12, I don't really see that happening. I really don't get how these female teachers seduce their young students. Frankly, it completely grosses me out. I like my men grown up, not wearing World of Warcraft underwear. I also like my men generally the same size as me, or bigger, not half my size, making me feel like a humongous Amazon.

But it got me thinking, soon I will be on my own, and able to sleep with anyone I wish. This is very interesting, and I never really thought about it before. Maybe I'll try eHarmony, seems like lots of people do that. Definitely not Farmers Only. Men who smell like manure has always been a turn off. I'd be a little bit afraid of meeting people online though, I've watched those Dateline "To Catch a Predator" things. I've seen all the incredibly creepy men who bring beer and condoms to their first date. Good God, if I went on a date and the man brought in beer and condoms, I would turn him around and boot him right in the ass crack. What are those morons thinking? Are there women, or young girls who think that's hot? For a dude to show up with beer and condoms? I find it repulsive. Presumptuous. Irritating. Gross. All those guys do is email photos of their genitals to girls, and think that is all the foreplay they need to do. What is that all about? Here's a photo of my ugly penis. And I'm sorry, they ARE ugly. Men's penises look much more enticing in a pair of sexy black jeans rather than naked in a Polaroid. I am not a good porn woman, probably another thing John hates about me. I can see the allure of "some" naked women, but men are pretty goofy looking naked. They have no butts, half the butt crack that women do. Too much hair equals very grizzly-esque. You KNOW if a man is hairy on the chest he's going to have a hairy ass crack. Too little hair equals too female-esque. Never wanted to date a swimmer due to that little issue. Not dating someone with smoother skin than me.

When I see naked men, I'm too distracted by how odd they look to ever be turned on by it. My thoughts of beer and condoms are interrupted by the pool man. Interesting...the pool man. I've never really thought about the pool man before, but suddenly, I am intrigued. His arms are tan and strong. I'd say he's probably about twenty? Twenty-five? I'm not so great with ages. He's trim but muscular. I watch him walk around the pool, pouring chemicals in. Then he gets his long brush and goes up and down in the pool. That's what she said!! (John and I always used to say that after anything that could be construed as sexual. Thanks to *The Office!*) He's starting to work up a sweat. Very interesting. Every brush of the pool brings a flex of his muscles. I start visualizing myself wandering out there in a bikini...no, wait...forgot about the stretch marks,

91

let's make that a one piece, with the sides cut out. Crap. Let's make it boy shorts and a tankini. And just remember to not turn sideways, I look a lot better from the front and back, not so hot from the side.

Ok, anyway, I'm looking hot in my boy shorts as I walk out the sliding door. (I have to feel sexy before I can have sex thoughts, just a quirk of mine. I don't do roll over in the morning, messy hair, morning breath, oily hair sex. Sorry. Morning sex is not sexy. I need to prepare this mom body for lovin' PRIOR to the lovin'.) I saunter outside with my tall glass of lemonade. The glass is sweating, dripping water down the sides because it's so hot outside. I lie down on the chaise lounge. Oh…I'm letting the water condensation drip from the glass into my belly button. Wait, is that sexy? Or is that gross? Let's call it sexy for the sake of my daydream here, OK?

He starts to glance at me every time he pulls his brush out of the pool to go down on another spot. OH! Ha ha…TWSS…that sounds terrible! But that's a good thing. I have sunglasses on, so he doesn't know I'm watching his every move. Suddenly he just stops, standing there, holding his pole (ha ha), looking at me. Sweating. Wait, maybe not sweating that much. That could be gross if he's a stinky sweater. Maybe just a bead rolling down the side of his temple. He puts his pole down. (Really doesn't get old does it?) He walks over to me, quietly as a cat…no, lion, king of the jungle. He sits down on my chaise lounge. Wait, he straddles the chaise lounge, sitting at the end of it. He starts massaging my feet. Crap, no! No foot massage...I HATE when people touch my feet. Feet are gross. He starts running a finger up and down my calf...but shit, I didn't shave and there is sparse blonde stubble. Grrrrr.

OK, he starts putting his hands on my inner thighs...oh Jesus...all I can think of is my loose, wiggly inner thighs. Damn, is there like anywhere on my body this make-believe pool man can touch me that doesn't gross me out?

Alright, the pool man starts rubbing my wrist. It's so sexy. I'm breathing so hard. No one has ever rubbed my wrist like this. It feels so wrong, but oh...OH...so very right. He rubs my wrist harder and harder...OK, this is so stupid I can't stand it. What the hell? How am I supposed to have some hot fantasy when the man in my fantasy can't touch any part of my body? I need to work out. This is ridiculous. I'm going to be a single woman soon! At least I won't have to worry about birth control, with men only having sex with my wrist. Now that is safe sex.

I snap out of my less than satisfying daydream and look out to the pool man, still going up and down with his pole. (Hee hee.) Suddenly, he stops and takes off his cap to wipe his sweat. Ewwwww! He's bald...and...OLD! He's not even young. He's like fifty! What? Who has a fifty year old bald pool boy? What little hair he has left above his ears is gray, and mashed down by the cap. His face is all red and wrinkled from the sun. Great. I sure can pick the hot ones to have my pretend affair with can't I? He's actually pretty repulsive.

Maybe I'm just destined to never have sex again. Maybe I'll always be single. Maybe I'll just be one of those old cat ladies, with hundreds of cats living in kitty squalor. Maybe I'm just supposed to be a sad, lonely old woman. By myself. Forever. Just me and my loose, wiggly inner thighs and sexy wrists.

We all have a little Nancy Kerrigan in us, when we wake up each day and ask "Why me?" From the smallest things in life - cable TV gets turned off for non-payment during the season finale of *So You Think You Can Dance*…to the larger things that truly matter, like your choice in a lifetime partner. I ask myself that question daily. Why me? Sometimes, when I'm feeling particularly strong-willed, I tell myself it's because God is testing me. Or that these bumps in the road of life are making me a stronger person. Sometimes I like to tell myself that I am a martyr, chosen by a higher power, to live this life of hell, with my hellish mate, and I will be rewarded greatly in the after life. In my next life perhaps, I will come back as a hot young celebrity, who gets to be a vampire in the movies and wear fancy dresses. Who gets her nails done and massages every week. Who graces the pages of People Magazine with a different amazingly hot young man every month. OH, and when I get pregnant, I will look so incredible, in tiny little shirts, cutoff shorts, and my iced decaf latte from Starbucks with my "baby bump" - instead of my "mom mountain". I imagine that my life will be so different, so wonderful, because I have endured what the gods have wanted me to endure in this life.

And when the Gods ask me if I have learned my lesson, I will answer yes. I hope I will be able to fool the Gods with that answer, because the truth is, I really don't know why I was chosen to lead this life. With a man who doesn't love me. A body that only lasted about twenty five years before it started to be sucked into the ground by earth's gravitational pull. The messiest children in the world. More bills than the average American family. Four dogs who never learned to use the great outdoors as their toilet. And a bathroom faucet that keeps me up all night with it's constant dripping. (Oh, you think my handy husband could repair that? Think again! Honey don't!)

The truth is, I'm bitter. I see so many happy people in the world and I don't understand why I can't be one of them.

The pool man collects his things and leaves. Which also means the dogs settle down and stop barking. There's a highlight to my day. There isn't much time where this house is quiet. A few years ago, it might have been the kids making noise, but now, it's either deafening screaming between John and I, or even worse, the loudest most grating silence you have ever heard. The silence of anger is a horrible silence. I know the kids hear it. I hate that they hear it. But as I just keep saying, I can't help it. There's no point in me dwelling on how this is affecting the kids right now, as it will just make me feel worse, and I don't want to feel any worse.

I am a little distracted right now. When you realize you have truly married the wrong person, it weighs heavy on the mind. When you have the clarity that divorce is imminent, it consumes you.

I had such great aspirations when I was single. Definitely not going to be like all those other couples that ended up sucking at marriage. I knew a woman growing up and when her husband got angry with her, she would just faint. Like a goat. She couldn't handle conflict and didn't communicate so she'd just faint.

I think people also hold grudges. Being married means being able to forgive and forget at the drop of a hat. Marriage dementia is a GOOD thing. If you can't remember why you were pissed an hour ago, you're doing great! Why do so many people hold onto the past like it's their last cookie? Clutching that anger and animosity until it crumbles in their hands.

Married people make up SO many excuses why their marriage doesn't work or why they had an affair. If you leave your home, and travel somewhere to actually have sex with another person when you're married, that's a pretty damn pussy ass thing to do. Either work on your marriage or get out! If you even think there could be such a thing as karma at ALL, how can you do that? I've always wondered how you go back home to your spouse, after that first time you've had an affair. That must feel like a 50 pound weight in your gut.

As a kid, I used to think that Elton John would change sides from being gay to wanting me. I was pretty much 100% convinced that Elton would have given up hot young men for me, a pimply fourteen year old. In my mind, it made perfect sense. I thought he was so hot during the *Caribou* time. I guess we'll never know will we. Then I moved onto Andy Garcia, at the *Untouchables* stage. Oh sweet mother, was he incredible looking in that movie or what? Put Kevin Costner to shame! Here's the crazy thing, I think I actually made eye contact with Andy Garcia once in Pasadena. In Old Town. Granted, he was getting into sort of an old, gray, Toyota, but I do think it was Andy. We had a moment. We stared into each other's eyes. No one believes me that Andy Garcia was in Pasadena, getting into an old car. However, reality is what you choose to believe. MY reality is that Andy and I made eye contact. There was something there. Even if it was only for two seconds.

My other fantasy love has been, and still is Trent Reznor. Before I got married, I fantasized all the time about how I would be at some party backstage. Trent would be so fed up with all the irritating groupie girls with their boobs flopping around and drunk talk, and he would see me. Someone different. Someone intelligent. Someone with something more to offer than just quick, backstage sex. Although, don't get me wrong, I had plenty of sex to offer Trent Reznor. Just not the "backstage" kind. Remember, I have to feel sexy while having sex. Sitting on an amplifier or beer soaked concrete isn't really going to get me all hot and sweaty.

I think I have always resented John because he wasn't Trent Reznor. Instead of a talented, sexy artist seemingly into S & M, I get an aging, beer gutted computer nerd, not sexy, into catching fish on little hooks and throwing them back into a large body of water.

What the hell happened to me? I married John. A man who runs people's computer systems. A man who watches the Discovery Channel, Man vs. Wild. A man who likes bagels and baked beans. Not one shred of excitement. Why did I settle? Why didn't I keep the dream alive and keep searching? OK, maybe Trent Reznor was a little unrealistic…though I still think if he had met me, there would have been something there…but anyone that brought at least SOME excitement to my life. I honest to God don't know what happened to me. How did I go from being convinced that Trent Reznor would fall in love with me, to marrying John? It is one of life's biggest mysteries to me. I think it's something I need to figure out in order to move on with my life. Why would I give any shot at an interesting life up for John? Love? I don't think so. I think I could have fallen in love with many men. I actually WAS in love with many different men. Why John? Did we have some amazing secret sex life? Was I constantly dressing up like a hooker and standing in front of Ralphs waiting for him to pick me up? Was it his incredible creativity that kept me captivated? Uh, well, he made me a card once, and cut out a picture of Brooke Shields and glued it on the card. The card said "You're hotter than Brooke". That's the most creative thing John ever did, and I took offense to it. Who gives you a card with Brooke Shields on it? Was it his hugely padded bank account, assuring I would always be secure financially and taken care of? We got married with virtually zero dollars in our savings account. After all these years, we are still living month to month. Some people don't want their kids to grow up because they are going to miss them, or they miss having babies. I'm scared to death our kids will grow up and want to go to college. Andrew is twelve and we have no college fund. So definitely didn't marry John for money. So what was it? I need to bring this up at therapy, because this question will kill me if I don't figure it out.

John, December 19th 3:30 p.m.

Bizarre day. My boss sent me home about an hour ago. He knows the stress I'm going through - he just divorced his wife about a year ago. He lets me work from home sometimes when he sees that I'm extra frazzled. I can hook up to the office computers by a VPN connection, works out great. Anyway, so I walked into our house and sat down on that odd love seat sofa that Denise bought. I put my head back to rest, and before I knew it, an hour had passed. I don't think I was sleeping, but I had some pretty crazy daydreams, I guess you'd call them.

I started thinking about what it will be like to be single. Hey, I'm a man. A man who hasn't had sex for five years, but still a man. I think. Let's put it this way, I have man parts. Whether or not they still work is the unanswered question. So I start thinking about…girls. Well, women. Adult ladies. Ladies? That sounds odd. "Ladies" sounds like I'm talking about my mother and I assure you, I'm definitely not talking about my mom. I find it so overwhelming the prospect of dating. Who do I date? Women at bars? Do I try to get involved at a church? I don't even have a church, I'm Jewish. Do I venture online? I'm just not into the whole online thing though. I know I'd fall in love with some amazing woman via email, only to meet her and she'd be hideous. I know a single mom at Andrew's school. I've seen her over the years. She's OK looking, not like lingerie catalog model amazing, but not bad. So I was sitting there on Denise's love seat, thinking about the single mom in Andrew's class.

I imagined we were on a date, dinner, not too fancy. Maybe California Pizza Kitchen. No, that's too bright, white and yellow. Maybe a little more romantic, like, say, Bucca de Beppo. Nah, that's too much food. Not so romantic if you're so stuffed you can't move. Maybe Denise is right, maybe I'm not romantic? No, I can be romantic. Denise is wrong. Whatever. I imagined an imaginary restaurant, just the right amount of lighting, and light food. I'll have to research restaurants later so I have some places to actually take women on dates.

So I'm there with the mom from Andrew's school. I really need to know her name because I really can't call her, hey "mom from Andrew's school". Let's say, for the sake of my daydream, her name is Page. I've always thought Page was a sexy name. So my daydream goes on, I am so clever and witty, making Page laugh at every other bite. I am *on*. Extremely charming. She can barely eat, she keeps laughing. I feel so amusing, so funny. I scoot closer to her in the booth. I can feel the warmth on my leg, coming from her thigh. I haven't felt warmth coming off a woman's body for a very long time. Just feeling that warmth, even imaginary warmth, began to stir things around inside me. Then, strangeness strikes. I reach for her hand, and take it in mine. I just want to hold a female hand. Want to look at it, touch it, hold it to my face. But the minute I touch the hand, it turns into Denise's hand. I would know Denise's hand anywhere. She has very soft hands, and they always smell good. Doesn't matter if she's doing dishes or digging in the garden, she has great smelling hands. Same freckle below her pinky finger. Same nails with the little white half moons in the nail bed. I let the hand go and opened my eyes. That's weird. Can't I have a nice little daydream without thinking of "the beast"? I was so calm and relaxed, determined to have me a nice little daydream…about a woman.

I think my choice of woman affected my daydream. Because I didn't know the mom from Andrew's school, she just morphed into Denise. Clearly, I needed to pick a different woman. I decided to go balls to the wall and pick the secretary at the law firm where I work. Why not? I'm a soon-to-be-divorced man, I can have daydreams about twenty three year olds, can't I? I know, it feels like the typical male, midlife crisis, looking to be with the hot young girl, but this is a DAYDREAM!

Her name is Rachel. She's really pretty hot. Twenty three, as I mentioned. Dark hair, about shoulder length. Total Victoria's Secret body. She's always fairly nice when I talk to her. Sometimes I think she doesn't hear me, but she's not rude. Her voice is a little high, squeaky but whatever. Can't have everything right? So, in my daydream, I imagined that Rachel and I went to the beach. I know, you're thinking I just want to have a daydream where I would see Rachel in a bikini…and, you're right. Oh well. What am I supposed to do? I think my male parts are all still functional. In my daydream, Rachel starts frolicking in the water. (Don't say anything!) I run up behind her, grab her around the waist, and strange beyond strange...I know I'm holding Denise. I know Denise's body. I know every curve. I know the heat that comes off her body. I know the feeling of her skin. There was some show on a while back, *Dating in the Dark*. Singles had to date in the dark, and some ended up falling for each other. However, during the reveal at the end, some bolted due to the physical looks of the person they had been dating in the dark. If Denise and I were on that show, I would only need to feel the warmth coming from her skin to know it was her. I can't believe how well I know that woman's body.

So here we go again. Rachel's hot Victoria's Secret body, has morphed into Denise's. There at the beach, in the water, I am holding Denise. I can't say that it feels bad either. But I am becoming frustrated. This isn't about Denise. Denise hates me. I just want to feel some "man feelings" and have a damn daydream. Is that too much to ask? Obviously I need to pull out the big guns here.

I closed my eyes and laid my head back on the weird love seat. Who? Yes. It has to be. Angelina Jolie. Who could be hotter? The woman hasn't aged for about 15 years. There definitely might be a little vampire going on there, because she's kinda scary too. Scary like you don't want to make her angry or else she'll belt you in the gut. Or bite your neck. And not a sexy biting of the neck. The kind of biting of the neck where your head is severed from the body and blood is spurting everywhere. But I digress. This was purely a normal male daydream, about Angelina and me, having drinks at a bar. OK, that is not a normal daydream, but you know what I'm trying to accomplish here, right? I just haven't had any feelings for Denise in so long, I just am trying to see if I can still, well, still be a man. Still have *those* feelings. Are we all on the same page? Yes? OK, thank you.

So Angelina and I are at some super cool Hollywood bar. Because it would have to be cool, if Angelina is going to go anywhere with me. Not like she'd agree to go to the Olive Garden or Sizzler. Maybe a hotel. Yeah, we're at the Standard, and it just so happens I have a room there also. We are down in the purple lounge, having Cosmopolitans. Well, she is. A Cosmo might be a little girly for a man. Even though I really like them. I'm having whiskey on the rocks. Nice. We are talking, (I have no idea about what, because really, what the hell are you going to talk to Angelina about?) I make a few clever jokes. Then, amazingly, I know, she says "You are so much funnier than Brad." This makes me smile, as I pride myself on my ability to make the ladies laugh. I can make Denise laugh. Well, I used to be able to make Denise laugh. Then Angelina says, "I never liked blondes" and runs her fingers through my hair. What's left of it. Up and around my ear.

For some reason, Angelina Jolie agrees to go up to my room. Thank God for daydreams, because this is so ridiculously far from reality. But, the minute I slide the room key, and walk through the door, I feel it. The heat of Denise's body brushes by me. The lights are still off in the hotel room, and she comes up against me. Doesn't touch me, just stands near me. The heat is overwhelming. It completely sucks me in. I feel like I want Denise so badly. I try to think of all of Denise's evilness and I can't quite get a handle on it. Denise just feels right, the heat. I know she's right in front of me and all I want to do is hold her. I open my eyes and stand up. Those feelings are feelings I haven't felt in years. Why am I feeling them now? I have never hated Denise more, and yet I'm sitting here having these deep feelings for her? It felt so real, feeling her body next to mine. I have been extremely clear in my resolve the past few weeks. To leave Denise. To be free of her. To move on. To find someone who will love me for who I am. Instead of things moving forward and becoming clearer, this happens. Sitting here, feeling that way towards Denise. It's very upsetting and confusing.

I came upstairs to write this, to get this out of me. I'm not really feeling better. I'm feeling confused. I feel the hatred for Denise slowly coming back into me, like when you have a limb waking up from being asleep. The hatred tingles as it seeps back into me. What is going on?

Denise, December 19th 5:00 p.m.

I'm exhausted. So tired. Sick of this whole situation I've gotten myself into. Before, suicide seemed like a way to get back at John. Now, suicide seems like a way out. I honestly don't know how long I can do this. It takes so much energy to hate. I feel tugged in every direction. I feel confused and I don't understand why I'm confused. Ten years of hatred isn't confusing. Yet, I am confused.

I was just downstairs, taking a rest on my new love seat. Trying to think about dinner. How absurd to have to stop my thoughts, about my life, my future, my non-marriage, my hatred for John, to think about dinner. I hate that life continues to move forward, even though we have very pressing situations. I've always felt that when our loved ones pass away, for example, time needs to stop. People can't continue to eat, go to work, drive, shop, enjoy life, when other people are hurting. Some of life is great, but some of it doesn't flow so well.

I feel so out of sorts. I was sitting there, trying to think of dinner. Here's what I thought of. Sushi. Sushi? I don't like sushi. Granted, when John and I were first dating, I'd eat avocado rolls and asparagus rolls. I don't eat asparagus rolls anymore. Once I got an asparagus roll, it was kind of pickled asparagus and it was utterly disgusting! But, I don't eat raw fish or any fish, so sushi to me, is no treat. It was just something I did for John, to be nice. A nice wife. A nice wife with no life, if I'm going the poetic route. So why was I sitting down there, and the only thing that came to mind was sushi? Something John loves? From sushi, my mind went to fishing. Fishing? Seriously? I went fishing once with John, when we were dating. I hate fishing. I'm a PETA supporter. I don't hurt any animals. And I don't buy that a fishhook in their little mouth doesn't hurt. Catch and release my ass. Yeah, we had fun on the fishing trip, but that was because we were together. We could have had fun sitting in a trash bin at that stage of our relationship. It wasn't because we were luring little helpless fish with their favorite food, so we could unhook their little mouths and toss them back in the water, in shock, with a hole through the roofs of their mouths.

And yet, all I could think about was fishing. How fun it was. I actually saw myself fishing with John. Now. I'm talking NOW. I had a vision. Us fishing. ENJOYING ourselves. I seriously believe I need medication, as I am feeling so far from myself it's freaking me out. I don't have control over my thoughts. What I am thinking goes in a completely different direction from what I think I want to think. Help.

Denise, December 19th 5:20 p.m.

Oh God. Wow. What? So I just told John I was making celery soup for dinner. Why? Because I know of all the things in this world, John hates celery the most. Personally, I've never understood that. Celery doesn't have much taste. Kind of tastes like water, maybe dirty water, but I like that crunchy, earthy taste. John must have been deeply scarred by celery as a child, because his aversion to it is off the charts.

So of course he goes off, as I knew he would.

Celery Hater: "Denise, you obviously want to make celery soup to piss me off. You are such a witch."

Soup Maker: "What? I'm making you dinner, and you call me a witch? Who's being the ass here?"

Celery Hater: "Jesus, you're only making celery soup to piss me off. Like you don't know I hate celery more than your mother?"

Soup Maker: "You're so full of hate. Let's make a list of everything you hate. Celery soup. My mother. Me…"

Celery Hater: "Ha! You're the hater! You hate everything. You are so miserable to be around. I've never known anyone so full of hate!"

That makes me twinge for a minute, I have to admit. See, I'm not used to being a hateful person. My grandmother had a heart full of love, and she shared it with everyone she met. So for me to be so full of hate is something I never wanted. I wanted to be like my grandmother. But John did this to me. This is not my fault.

Soup Maker: "You need to look to yourself. You really do. All you do is point the finger at me, never, ever looking at yourself. It's so easy to say it's the other person's fault."

I can see that had a tiny affect on John. He pauses for half a second. I've become an expert at shoving the crap of an argument back on his plate. Keeping my plate clean. Letting him deal with the scraps. Not letting anything dry and get stuck on my plate. It's much easier to keep things clean and clear in my head that way.

He sighs and then sits on the love seat. That really pisses me off. Why does he keep sitting on that? I bought it. It's mine. He acts like he likes it. Hello!? It was meant to piss him off, and he keeps sitting on it? That pisses ME off! So I march over and sit down on the other cushion of the love seat, as close to the arm as I can. I plop down and it makes John rise up on his side. I find that way more amusing than it should be. Suddenly I am overcome with hysteria. But I have to try to keep it in. Keep it together Denise. I hate this man. This man hates celery. He doesn't want my soup anymore. And when I say soup, I mean everything I have to offer.

I turn my head to the side, so he can't see laughter seeping out between my lips. Then...he busts out laughing! I can't stop it. Suddenly all my anger is directed at myself for my lack of self-control. There we are, laughing on the love seat. Can I just say, WHAT THE HELL!

Sitting here is probably one of the strangest experiences I've had in my life. I feel like I have no control over my emotions and that everything in my body is being pulled towards the light. Towards happiness. I haven't sat this close to John, (even though there is about three feet between us) in a very long time. He almost looks…handsome? Oh no, "Take My Breath Away" from Berlin is playing on the TV…that song always gets me. GRRR STUPID *TOP GUN*! I hate that a movie with Tom Cruise in it affects me so much.

John: "That was a fun ride".

I laugh.

John: "Do you know what we're doing? What's going on here?"

I have to think a very long time, to get my thoughts together. I want to blurt out, yes, we are getting a divorce, but my mouth will not make those words. They won't come out. Finally I speak.

Me: "I think we're confused."

But I don't mean that! I'm not confused. Or, rather, I haven't been confused, until the past couple of days. I've known exactly what I was doing and what I wanted. Until now. But. OK, I'm confused.

Me: "My thoughts are so all over the place."

John: "Me too. Which leads me to think that perhaps we shouldn't make any decisions until our thoughts are crystal clear. We can't go making decisions like this, without being completely 100% certain."

Hold on here. Does he mean what I think he means? Is John trying to say that we shouldn't move forward in getting a divorce? Could that possibly be? Is he completely insane? We HATE each other. Anyone could tell you that. Everyone knows it. Even the kids want us to get divorced.

Me: "What are you saying John?"

But, suddenly my thoughts wander again. No, I'm definitely not in control of my thoughts. I have the split TV screen thing going on. It starts out with television shows playing, oddly, all reality shows. The TV zooms in on Phil from *The Amazing Race*. He fills the screen on the fake television in my imagination. Strangely, it's not a flat panel. It's an old style box. Then Phil starts talking to me. "I'm sorry to tell you, you're the last couple to arrive."

Obviously he is talking to me. Looking right at me, so I talk back.

Me: "What are you talking about?"

Phil: "I'm happy to tell you, this is a non-elimination round of the race. You're still racing!"

Me: "What? We are?"

Phil: "However, you're going to have to pick it up, because in the next round, you will encounter a roadblock that only you and John will have to do."

Me: "A road block?" That makes me chuckle. "John and I have experienced more road blocks than just about any couple I know!"

Phil: "You're going to really need to get your act together now, your race depends on it."

Me: "Are you talking about our marriage Phil?"

Phil: "I think we've all felt your pain through out this race, but I also think we have all seen the potential in you as a team. You all just need to work together, rather than fight against each other. We all believe in you."

Me: "You do?"

Phil: "Yes we do, and good luck."

Me: "Thanks Phil".

John: "Who's Phil?"

Huh? Suddenly I'm back on the sofa. I just sit there, staring at the television.

John: "Denise? Who's Phil?"

Clearly he thinks I'm losing it.

Me: "You know, Phil from *The Amazing Race*."

Suddenly John starts laughing. Hysterically. I start, for half a second, to be annoyed at him, because it seems like he's laughing at me. But then, I completely understand that he's laughing with me. Like he understood that Phil from *The Amazing Race* was just giving me marriage advice. I couldn't help it. I start laughing.

Oh God. What does that feel like? I can't even express to you. To be sitting there, laughing hysterically. With John. After so long, so many years of hatred, and stress, and anxiety. Laughing. It cleanses your soul. It lifts your heart. It makes you healthier. It feels soooooooo good!

I'm looking at John, things I hate about him aren't there. It's like a dense fog that has been covering him is breaking apart. I'm seeing parts of him that I haven't seen since we were first married. I find myself concentrating on his eyes. They are really, truly kind. I'm shocked I don't see this every day. They have nothing but sweetness in them. Happiness. John's eyes? I try to get in touch with my hatred for him, which I know is there, it's been there forever. But I can't find it. It's completely gone. Then, our eyes meet. His are a magnet, mine are iron ore. Even if someone offered me one million dollars at this very moment, I could not look away from John's eyes. It's a spectacular feeling to be held in place by someone's eyes, unable to blink or look away. It's an intense power that makes your heart race. We still have leftover fading smiles on our faces from the whole Phil – *Amazing Race* thing. Smiles are fading, yes, but our faces of frustration and hatred are not returning. Faces of…of…faces of…love? Did I just say LOVE? Love! John is looking at me. Then, I realize. I know why I fell in love with him. True he wasn't Trent Reznor. Didn't have a ton of cash, fancy cars, and an unending supply of hair atop his head. But, what he did have, his mutant power, was how he looked at me. THAT is why I fell for him. THAT LOOK. The one he is giving me now. The look that makes my shoulders twitch and neck constrict. The look that causes my stomach to tingle and the back of my neck to start to sweat. I can't even lift my arms at the moment. THAT LOOK makes me weak. How is a man with sparse hair and not in the best shape, able to do that with his eyes? That is one powerful look. I had no idea John still had that in him.

At this moment, John slides his hand over on top of mine. A zap of electricity flies up my arm and into my brain. This man has not touched me…for years? It is such an immediate shock to my system that the eye contact is broken. From the looks of it, it also shocks him. I am sure if I look at my arm, I'll see burn marks from being zapped. I have actually grabbed a live wire in my life, when I was a kid, but this is WAY more intense. What you would expect a defibrillator to feel like. I stand up, pulling my hand out from under his. I can't speak. I just look at him, then turn and walk upstairs.

I am numb. The hate that usually washes over me so quickly is like honey now. Only *slowly* flowing back in. With difficulty. Then…it happens. The last ten years begin playing in filmstrips on each side of my head, zooming at me, so quickly the normal human couldn't make heads or tails of the scenes. I can, because it is my life. Ten years zip by each side of my face, my eyes darting back and forth. Understanding all. I swear there is wind on my face from my life rushing past me in filmstrips. It stops. The last frame, on each side…is…the love seat.

I sprint downstairs, skip every other stair, and slip and slide on my butt for the last five stairs. I don't even feel the bruise-to-be on my tailbone. I turn the corner into the living room, or rather slide around the corner barely hanging onto the wall. John is still sitting on the love seat when we both say at the same time, "THE LOVE SEAT!"

I rush and plop down on it. Breathing so fast. He is breathing fast too, even though he has been sitting. We both understand. At the same time. It is so clear. I have goosebumps all over my body, and slightly teary eyes. I look down at this small, ugly and quite magical love seat. I feel the fabric with my hand. It feels like any normal sofa fabric. And yet, it is far from it. John speaks first.

John: "So…when we are both on this…love seat…"

I end up taking quite some time to finish his sentence. I mean, I know how to finish it from the minute he speaks it. But to actually say these words out loud, takes some effort. I keep looking at the fabric, running my hand over it. Then he puts his hand back over mine, and that gives me what I need to finish the sentence.

Me: "Everything is perfect…"

John nods. We look into each other's eyes for about 27 minutes. Andrew walks in the room, sees our hands on top of each other…and promptly turns and runs out. He probably thinks John is grabbing me to finish me off. So silly. Clearly the last thing on this man's mind is hurting me. I break the silence.

Me: "How can this be? How can this possibly be? We sit on this love seat, and we are our old selves? We are in…"

I can't say it. I think it. But I get stuck when it comes to actually saying it. It's been soooooooo long. My heart is pounding so hard. I am nervous, but a GREAT nervous. Like John and I are on a first date. This is exhilarating. Wonderful. He says it.

John: "Love."

John then takes my hand in both of his and moves about 4 inches closer to me.

John: "Let me just talk out loud for a minute. Get my thoughts out and see if you are thinking the same thing."

I nod.

John: "Ok, I've been having emotions all over the place lately. Emotions that go from hating you to loving you more than I ever have."

Hearing him say that makes me have to concentrate on my breathing so I don't faint. "Loving me more than he ever has??" Oh…my.

John: "And now I understand that every time I've had these intense feelings for you, it has been while I have been sitting on this love seat. Therefore, we can conclude, that this love seat…"

Now *he* is the one that can't finish his sentence. I find it very cute. I know John is more of the analytical brain, and has never been one to believe in magic, psychics, vampires, aliens or anything that cannot be proved. I know how hard this is for him to grasp.

Me: "Is magical…somehow."

John nods.

Me: "It does make sense now! Every time I get up and go upstairs, I feel the hatred for you again."

John winces at hearing me say that. "The hatred for him". Then I crinkle my nose as I understand how horrible that sounds. Then he chuckles at me.

John: "God I love when you do that. So damn cute."

My heart has not stopped beating quickly, and now surges again. John just said…something about me…is cute!? I feel like every part of my body is fluttering and on fire. I can't take deep breaths. I feel like I'm barely holding on to reality. This overwhelming love feeling, and...desire? Woah! DESIRE? As in...I want to BE with John? In THAT way? Oh... my...God!

John: "Denise".

He says my name and I almost lose it. I feel like I'm 17 and on a date with a guy that I've been dying to go out with. Every feeling is new, and fresh, and intense, and AMAZING. John smiles, I think he understands how I feel. I think he's feeling the same way. But look at him. He's in control. He's not some wimpy ass guy repairing computers. He's a man. He knows what he's doing. He has a look in his eyes...he's perfect. He can control a room with that look. Not to mention me. I can't believe I haven't fainted yet.

John: "I want to try something. We are going to stand up, and walk upstairs and we are not going to let go of each other, OK?"

I would do anything he asked me to right now, so I just nod my head. I am powerless over that look in his eyes. We stand up and begin to walk upstairs. We are about seven stairs up, when I look at my hand in his, and with out any thought, I yank my hand away. We stop on the stairs and make eye contact. I feel...some...negative thoughts coming back. Suddenly I get flashes of birthdays missed, anniversaries spent bathing children and doing laundry, of screaming at each other in front of the kids. At the same time, we both turn around and race back to the love seat.

John: "Well then. It's true. While we are sitting on this love seat, we are who we are supposed to be. When we get up, the fog of life surrounds us, making it impossible to see the true love we have for each other through the clouds."

That makes me sigh out loud. He is so beautiful. What a way with words. I nod my head in agreement.

John: "So, Denise, I for one, do not want to leave this love seat. The way I feel for you, while sitting here, is what is right. I don't know why I can't feel this way in any other location. But this is right. I know it. This is how you and I are supposed to be. This is our destiny. We were meant for each other. This love has obviously always been here. The universe was trying to trick us. We outsmarted the universe Denise. We know the truth now. We understand we are supposed to be together always. You know this. What we have is beyond an earthly love. It's a bond that has always been there. Forces came very close to destroying us. But no more. I will never let you go. YOU are my love. YOU are my destiny. YOU are the entire sole reason I exist. I want nothing more than your happiness and to fulfill your desires. You are beauty. You are the definition. You make me feel like light. So bright and clear. There is not one other woman in this world that could possibly do this to me."

My eyes are so full of tears. I'm trying not to blink. It would be an immediate ocean running down my face. I'm in physical shock at his words. My entire body is cold and clammy and hot and sweaty. A great, huge rush of fear jolts through me at the thought that I almost threw him away.

Me: "John, I can't believe this was inside us this whole time. What if we had gone forward? What if we had gone through with it? What if we missed this? What if we never got this love seat? What…"

I'm interrupted with John's lips on mine. He was holding my hand in his hand, then put his other hand on my back and pulled me closer to him. The ocean explodes down my face… washing over our lips. You don't understand. The last time we kissed…was YEARS ago. But, this isn't just some "See you later honey" type kiss. This is filled with passion, and heat and tears and spice. It is the Sriracha kiss! Intensity beyond what humans should actually experience while kissing. I feel like my heart is on the verge of a heart attack. I know my heart is at least triple it's usual size.

John: "I don't know how this is going to work, with life, my job, the kids…but clearly Denise, we cannot leave this love seat."

Andrew, December 19th 8:40 p.m.

So, yeah. I just went down stairs to see if anyone was giving any thought to making dinner for the three kids in this house, and there is something beyond freaky going on here. Mom and Dad… were…KISSING!!!!!! WTF!!!! And when I say WTF, I mean WTF!!!!!!!!!!!!!!!!!! I can't even comprehend this. I mean, what is going on here!? This makes no sense. My mom hates my dad. Dad hates Mom. That's the way it is here. It's been that way ever since I can remember. How can they be sitting down there kissing! This can't even be happening. We all have accepted our parents suck, we will be the offspring of divorced parents, being shuffled back & forth between houses, having new girlfriends wanting us to call them "mom", leaving our backpacks at the wrong house on a Monday morning. What is this!! How can they be kissing! It ruins everything! This is disgusting! Ugh…I guess I'll sneak down and make something for the girls. This sucks. OMG my mom is yelling for me now! Guess I'll go see what she wants.

I get downstairs and I see them. Holding hands. Sitting next to each other. Like touching. WTF!!!! Smiling? I swear, they look happy. Drugs? My parents are on drugs? Druggies. They're the ones who told me about the commercial about your brain being a fried egg in the pan. They don't take their own advice? This is seriously freaky!

Mom: "Honey, we need you to get us a few things, OK? Can you get us both our laptops and cell phones. And, if you wouldn't mind, there are frozen pizzas in the freezer, just pop them in the oven and there's premade salad in the fridge. Tell the girls to take their baths while the pizza is cooking. I would *REALLY* appreciate it Andrew."

Me: "Mom…Dad…what is going on here? What is this? Why do you two look happy?"

Dad: "Andrew, we are happy. We have always been happy…with each other, we just didn't know it, we didn't have the capability to understand it."

Me: "So what are you saying, like, you're staying together? Not getting divorced."

Dad: "No Andrew, we are not getting divorced. We are very much in love."

Dad then kisses Mom's hand and looks in her eyes. OMG this is so bizarre! They look like different people when they smile. I am so used to seeing my mom frown and be mad, she actually looks pretty. This makes *me* smile. My dad pats the love seat next to him as he scoots closer to my mom. There isn't a lot of room but I squeeze in next to him. He puts his arm around me.

Dad: "Andrew, I know we have been about the worst parents in the universe. Totally selfish, concentrating on being angry at each other instead of being parents. I know we haven't been there for you or the girls. We both regret that so very much. All we can do is move forward from this point, and be there for all three of you. It's going to change Andrew. I promise you that. We ARE there for you now. Only hitch is, we kind of have to stay on this love seat."

I feel my Dad's arm around me and it feels warm and makes me happy. I look past him to my mom, her face. They are both so happy. It fills me with hope. Hope for them, hope for my life, my sisters. Hope that we could actually be a normal family. Like in movies. No more screaming. Anger. Rage. Mean words. I feel the change. In both of them. I see it. Suddenly, sitting here, next to my mom and dad, I feel the happiest I've felt in a long time. Wait…what!?

Me: "Dad, what did you just say? You have to stay on this sofa?"

Dad chuckles a bit and looks at Mom, then back to me.

Dad: "Yes, well, see, there is something about this love seat. When your mom and I are sitting on it, we have clarity. We can be how we were meant to be together. There is no hatred. No regret. No junk to sift through. We feel the love that we felt the first day we met. But, when we stand up, all the junk comes back and in no time, we hate each other again. So, until we come up with a better solution, we want to stay here."

Me: "What about work? Driving us to school? Everything? Life?"

Dad: "Yeah, well, we're working on it. It won't be easy, but we will figure it out. The good news is…there will be no more screaming or arguing in this house."

Wow. I look up at the ceiling to think about this for a second. No more screaming or arguing in this house. Really!? This is a miracle. I've hated coming home from school day after day. I've never had "parents", in my opinion. I've just lived with two people who hated each other. This is AMAZEBALLS!

Me: "So, you guys…this love seat…it's magical? Or something?"

Mom and Dad laugh at this.

Mom: "Yep, it appears that it is. We even tested it. We got up, made it to about the seventh stair over there, and the feelings of hatred started coming back."

Me: "Woah…that is crazy! Sooooo Hogwarts! OK, OK, don't worry, I'll take care of everything. You guys just stay there. Do NOT move! This is freaking awesome. STAY THERE!"

Mom and Dad are laughing again as I run off into the kitchen to make dinner. I put the pizza in and race upstairs to talk to my sisters. I go into their room and tell them of the totally bizarre but pretty awesome stuff that is going on downstairs. It's funny, they have no problem with accepting that suddenly a magical love seat is saving the day, making my mom and dad be in love again. Me? Well, I have a problem with it. I don't understand it. But, on the other hand, I'm REALLY happy this is happening.

Oh, and Mom asked me how my day was. She hasn't done that in a very long time. :)

Denise, January 4th

Well, the kids are back to school after the holiday break. I guess I have been neglecting getting my thoughts out, for a good reason of course.

If someone had told me six months ago that John and I would be spending our days on a small love seat and completely and utterly happy with each other, I would have laughed in their face and maybe I would have slapped them. Slugged them? I don't know. The truth is, I have never been happier. I don't understand how this is happening. I tried calling the store where this love seat came from. That adorable Asian man. Unfortunately I didn't remember the name right, I guess. My Mandarin is a little rusty. No such shop exists. And, of the hundreds of receipts I have from that day of "rage shopping", oddly I have nothing from that store. We were able to send a ton of it back, thus salvaging John's pristine credit. Hahaha. Oh…I was in a terrible place wasn't I? Wow. I can't even get in touch with any thought that might hurt or harm John now. This love seat holds a strong and powerful magic.

I'm looking up over the top of my laptop at him now. Look at that man. The man I love. The man I married. The man I took that slow motion walk down the aisle to. That was one magical moment. All the preparation for the wedding. All the pleasing both sets of parents. That was my moment. When they opened the doors and I saw him. Standing there. With his hands grasped in front of him. White rose on his black tuxedo. Looking at me. That was MY moment. The walk. Honestly I believe it lasted an hour. My steps were so small, I don't even think they were steps. I think I was on an extremely slow moving walkway. Like at the airport. Everyone else in that church became blurry nonexistent background images. Just John and I. Eye contact the entire time. No blinking at all. He had the ever-so-slight smile on his face. There are few moments like that in life. When it's just you, and another person. Eye contact. You feel the sting of not blinking. You feel the dryness across your eyes and yet, you are entranced. You can't pull your eyes away. Huge emotion. Heart beating out of your chest. You know you want that person. And I'm not just talking sex. You *want* that person. You want all of them. You want their hands on you. You want to be in their head. You want to be near them but far enough away to take them all in. You want to breathe their essence, what makes them human. You want to taste their different tastes from tears to their neck. You want their heat. You want their mind.

For some women, weddings are all about the dress. What you wear. The cake. The centerpieces. The words you say to each other. For me, it was and will always be that walk, to John. Burned into my memory. Finally getting to him. Him putting his hand out to me. Taking me, from my previous life before him. Taking me to him. Beginning a life together. A stunning moment.

And now I look at him. Makes me smile. He's on his laptop, I'm on mine. His legs are on the outside, mine are on the inside. We are crammed on this little love seat, for the sake of love. Makes me laugh. Look at what we're willing to put ourselves through, for love. Ahhhhh love! So worth fighting for. I was such an idiot. Ready to toss it out with the apple cores.

It's amazing how hate can blind you. So difficult to see past hatred when you are wrapped up in it. I really must try to remember this in my life if I ever get to a place like that again. To stop, in the middle of the hate, and try to get outside of it. Things are so much clearer when you don't have a head full of hate. Happens way too often to people. So many marriages given up on…because they couldn't get out. Stuck in the muck of hate and routine.

So the past couple of weeks have been pretty…different. Once the kids realized that this was real, that John and I are actually getting along, not screeching at each other, and in love again, they jumped on board.

Day to day living, on a love seat, isn't the easiest thing you know. Thankfully I had bought half of Los Angeles, and I kept enough presents so that the holidays weren't an issue. I wrapped and wrapped from my little space on the sofa. During the day, John sits on his side and I on mine. He does his work, I manage the house and kids from my side. When John told his boss he was working his marriage out, but needed to work from home, his boss was more than accommodating! John has been going above and beyond the call of duty for that company because we are so thankful they are letting him work at home!

Andrew is the best kid ever. Helping with his sisters, their meals, making sure they take baths, doing laundry then bringing it to me to fold. Here's what's funny - when you hate the world, you hate laundry. When the world holds happiness for you, laundry isn't so bad. Ok, what the hell am I saying. Laundry sucks whatever your mental state. John has always said the key is "disposable clothing". I think he's onto something.

We've moved everything we can near the sofa. Phone chargers, microwave, coffee maker, bottled water, TV, table, small fridge that was in the garage. Our living room doesn't look so attractive but oh well. Price you pay for happiness! I have gotten my friends across the street to take the kids to and from school. They have kids about the same age. I just told her I have a medical condition and I cannot leave the house. Basically true. If I leave, I will hate John, causing my blood pressure to skyrocket, then I will explode and die. (Or kill myself...) But I think my neighbor thinks I'm a vampire and she's only driving the kids for me so I won't turn her...to an undead. I'm a little pale and my canine teeth are pretty sharpish. Every time I talk to her I try to turn the conversation somehow to vampires. Just to keep her on "board". (Winky winky.)

Don't even ask, because I know you're wondering. You're saying to yourself, "Denise, HOW do you and

John go to the bathroom?" LOL! I knew you were thinking that. Well, there are certain times when of course we cannot be on this love seat. Mainly showers and using the toilet. Our downstairs guest bathroom is off the front hallway, probably about, um…20 feet away? I'm terrible with measurements. (Here is where John would always insert a crude joke… I'll leave it up to your imagination.) So we have a system. We get on our cell phones, and basically, one talks to the other one the entire time. We are making sure our diet includes a lot of fiber, so no bathroom trip takes too much time. TMI? Well, you wanted to know. We decided the person going to the bathroom can't speak. Only listen. I've broken that rule a few times, bringing up the past, calling John a "jerk" from the loo when "those" feelings start swarming back into my brain. But John is usually able to talk over me, stays strong and reminds me that it's just forces beyond our control. Once he did have to rush to the bathroom when I was exiting and pull me back to the love seat. I was ready to march upstairs and down the hall to hatred.

Showers work much the same way. We have this little ledge that holds a candle outside the guest shower. So we put our cell phones there on speaker. It's like some sort of weird stereo because I can hear John yelling from the living room, and on the cell phone. This morning I was in the shower and it seemed different. I really concentrated on his words, rather than on the fear that the hatred would return. He told me about this time when we were dating and we went to the mall. I do, well call it what you will, fun? Impulsive? Creative? Bizarre?...things at times. At least, I used to. As I showered, I kept my eyes on the phone that sat on the tiny decorative ledge.

John: "Remember that time, when we were dating? We went to that mall, in Thousand Oaks. You gave me a tiny kiss and told me to have a seat in the fancy dresses section. As I sat there, I was actually getting a tiny bit turned on, I have to admit. I'd never had a girl tell me to have a seat while she tried on clothes for me. It was super sexy. The fantasies started as soon as I sat down. I imagined you coming out in a black, tight, dress...straps or no straps really didn't matter. I imagined you turning around, smiling at me, your hair following your turn in a sweeping flair. I looked up and down your body, as you turned. Yes, I apologize that it was the 'tight black dress' fantasy, but I think most guys fall prey to that one."

That made me laugh in the shower. My head was so ultra-sudsy, shampoo bubbles piled up about seven inches, I just didn't want to rinse it off and miss any of this story.

John: "Well, you can only imagine Denise, where my dressing room fantasy went from there. I was having some pretty intense emotions sitting there waiting for you at Macy's. Always loved that store.

"So Denise, when you walked out in that horrific, bright yellow and lime green lacy mother-of-the-bride dress, your red tennis shoes showing their tips from underneath the chiffon edge, the thick puffy sleeves swallowing your shoulders, I honestly about exploded. It was such a shock to my system. Firstly, I was expecting sexy and I get my Aunt Esther. But there was the girl I was falling in love with, in the most hideous dress I'd ever seen. I guess in a weird way, it was sexy, because all I wanted to do was rip that god-awful dress off of you.

"I remember bursting out with laughter. But, it's not what you're thinking. I actually wasn't laughing at how funny the situation was. How most girls would want to try on something sexy to impress a guy. How I happened to somehow get a girl that was contrary to the world. That although she had put on the ugliest, most disgusting dress she could find, she looked absolutely adorable. I was laughing, and it was nervous laughter, because I knew then, at that moment, I never wanted to lose you. I knew, seeing you in your yellow chiffon, that I would have to work hard to keep you entertained and happy in our life together. It was a challenge, but one I knew I wanted to accept at that moment, sitting in that peach vinyl chair, in the dress section of Macy's. It's one of my favorite memories Denise, the moment of knowing you want to spend your life with someone. Probably for most guys, it happens during sex, or in some amazing location. For me, it was Macy's. And, um, I have to admit, it's why I always shop for you at Macy's. You know I'm not a shopper. Not my "thing". But, I have no problem going into that store."

I had such a huge smile on my face. I didn't even know how long I'd been in the shower. The water from the shower head washed the single tear that came out of my eye down my body to the drain. I didn't have any feelings of hatred coming back in. My hands were soooo water logged all crinkly and wrinkly. I was so, SO concentrated on his voice and what he was telling me. It was a different sensation. It was easy to keep the negative feelings out.

Anyway, that's how our bathroom trips go. One of us reminding the other about wonderful times and memories. It's funny. Why can't couples do this...normally? Showering is a good time for this. You have the captive audience of the person bathing. The other is free to talk and express their feelings. I think too many couples just move on in life...constantly moving apart, rather than making that tiny effort to keep the connection strong. Every couple on this planet has memories. Good times they've had together. The power of those memories is a magic that couples forget to use. Reminding the person you are with of those memories is so very powerful. How you felt during those times.. I'm learning things I never knew about John, simply by him telling me his side of these memories. So many look back on early memories as a time and a place that they can never get back to. They mourn for how "it used to be" when things were fresh and new, instead of getting in touch with those incredible feelings and realizing...and REALIZING, those feelings are STILL there! The years can be cruel to a relationship. Time wraps memories in a fog. It's not that difficult to turn the fog lights on and see through it. So much love, still there. So many memories. Still there. Life isn't all about looking forward to the next thing that will make you feel good. It's about looking behind you also. Remembering how you got here. Paying attention to the small things that got you here today. Always remembering…holding on. Being strong. It's so simplistic and shallow to think the grass is greener. It's so complicated, intricate, and brilliant to realize what you have is greater than anything you might be fooled and lured away by.

Probably the most amusing thing that happened during the holiday break was when we had my parents, Barb and Steve, over for Christmas. They had invited us to their place but of course, not being able to leave the love seat makes travel a teeny bit difficult. When John suggested we have them over to our house, to see the kids, exchange presents, etc. I admit I had a mini-freak out. My mother, is…an…interesting woman. She loves me and the kids so much, but she's always been suspicious of John. I mean she loves him and is wonderful to him, but if you told her "actually, John has been running a prostitution ring, selling crack, and running a small terrorist sleeper sell", she would be the first to say "I knew it!" She has one tone in her voice when she address the kids and me, and a separate tone when she speaks to John. It's only slightly lower, and a teeny tad slower. Not as obvious as when Jerry says "Newman", but along those lines.

I've always admired how John is unfazed by my mom. But John reassured me and said "If all else fails, we will squish them on this love seat with us and I will fall madly in love with your mom." Ok, GROSS, but when you're laughing that hard, it's difficult not to agree to things.

The kids did the best they could to help straighten up, but there was no getting our living room looking "normal". People just don't have microwaves, mini-fridges, computers, TV's all packed into the center of their living rooms. People also usually, don't spend most of their lives sitting on a tiny love seat. Urgh. I was super nervous about my mom assessing our "situation".

The kids greeted them at the front door, and brought them over to where John and I were sitting. We stood up, hugged and it was so awkward because my mother started to move in beside me, to sit next to me on the love seat, but John just plopped down. She came THIS close to sitting in his lap. Andrew offered my mom a chair to distract her from the almost lap dance. She had this confused look on her face...the first of many to come during their visit.

At first, it all seemed fairly normal, as my parents sat on chairs between the microwave and the mini-fridge. The kids just stood, with their arms around Mom and Dad. I knew it was coming. My mom has forever and always wanted to break me off from the group and talk about John. Take me off into the bedroom. Get me alone. Ask me if "'everything is ok." Make some underhanded reference like, "well, if things aren't working out, just come home." Nothing she'd like better, so she could have complete control over the kids and my life. My mom stood up and gave me the nod, as in "lets head into the kitchen and have a girl chat". John also knew this was coming and averted her plot by reminding me to tell my dad about the huge bass I caught at Clear Lake. (My dad is a big fishing nut.) My mom seemed mildly irritated that she didn't get her way and sat back down in her chair next to the cancer-causing microwave.

Thank god Dad took over saying, "Denise really? You? How big was it? 20? 25 pounds? More? What was the coloring? Do you know what type it was?"

I really didn't have a chance to say anything because my dad just went off with about fifty questions about the nonexistent bass fish. I've never even eaten a bass fish much less caught one. Which John knew. John looked slightly amused with his choice in distraction topics.

One thing about my mom, she's not interested in anyone speaking about a topic she cares nothing about. If the topic should turn to fishing, poetry, drones, clogging, crocheting, or water purification, she just gets this look of frustration on her face. She doesn't have the patience to sit there and pretend to be interested in meaningless topics. She kept semi-wincing and looking at my dad, trying to will him to stop speaking. My dad, knowing the effect of her powerful glares, never let his eyes move towards her location. He just kept on, explaining the differences of various types of bass fish. How fresh water differs from salt water. The different types of bait. Finally, she'd had her fill and just began talking right over my dad. Awww, poor Dad. He just drifted off mid-sentence and sunk back into his chair.

My mom began her big story about going to Costco. Okay...

Mom: "So your father and I went to Costco to see if they had a rug for our family room. I'm telling you that place is a zoo. I feel like I need a shower when I come out of that place. I really had to knock some heads together to get what I needed. You know how we need a new rug for our family room? Well, I thought Costco might have a good option. By the time we got to the rugs your dad had filled the cart with the craziest things that we did not need!"

She shot him a look as he sunk down further into his chair.

Mom: "Your dad just gets sucked in by the silliest things. We don't need a hand blender or a back massager mat! Anyway, we finally make it to the rugs which are at the back of the store and there is no one around to help us. They had those rugs just piled up. In one pile! How are you supposed to see the rugs at the bottom? Those rugs weigh a ton. I told your father to go get someone to help us, but he just wandered around and came back with a sausage sample for me. *I* finally had to go find someone which took about ten minutes. I pulled a girl off her register and demanded she help me!"

Andrew is rolling his eyes, the girls are uninterested and John is nodding at my mom, like he is seriously relating to her story or something. I give him a "WTF" look. He winks at me.

Mom: "So finally we get back to the rugs. The girl, that had walked a mile to the back of the store with me, looks at the rug pile and has the nerve to tell me she can't help me! I then demanded to speak to her supervisor. When that person came out I demanded to speak to their supervisor. Until finally I talked to "Raymond", the supervisor of all of the Southern California Costco's who just happened to be in the store that day! He was so nice, just the sort of person you want to be in charge."

My mom always seems to attract the "top people" where ever she goes. Whether that's speaking to the person at the TOP of Costco, or the OWNER of the restaurant, or the MANAGER of the store. If there's someone in charge, they will be find their way to my mom. My mom has no use for those not in a power position.

Mom continues: "Raymond gave me his personal contact number in case I have any further issues at Costco. Do you know he got a fellow to drive a fork lift over and lift up all those rugs so I could see the one on the bottom? It didn't fit with our color scheme in the family room but how sweet was Raymond?"

After the Costco story was over she made another move. She started upstairs and called for me to follow, saying that she needed to borrow some hand cream. Andrew, so sharp, darted up the stairs in front of her telling her he'd show her where some hand cream was. I glanced at her to see her shoot me a frowny face. This would all be very funny if I wasn't so stressed out about trying to stay on this love seat!

My mom came back downstairs. OH MY GOD, her hands were tinged green. She kept wiping them together, and the more she did that, the more green crumbly stuff came off her hands. Great. Andrew had given her some of my avocado facial mask stuff for her hands, I kept it in a plastic container on the counter. Guess you can't really expect a tween boy to know the difference between a facial mask and hand cream. I noticed green fingerprints and a lipstick mark on Andrew's cheek. Poor kid. He has worked so hard to help us. I hope he has a wonderful life and one love, and never has his heart broken. I'm going to make it up to him, what we've put him through over the past years. I feel such extreme guilt, more so for Andrew than the girls even. I guess because he's older and "gets it". Gets the crushing sadness and hopelessness of living in a house with parents who despise each other. Gets the loneliness of really not having parents at all. No one to ask you about your day, school, or even make you dinner. Wow, we sure let him down. It's so incredible how easy it is to be selfish when you are having marriage problems. It actually felt "OK" to neglect my own children. Damn, I will never ever let that happen again. That hurts. I never wanted to be "that" mom, that didn't give a crap about her kids.

I guess I can't kick myself over and over for this. The best I can do is learn from my huge ass mistake and be the best mom I can to these kids during the very limited time I have left with them before they begin their own adventure of life.

The picture started getting a little obvious to my mom - that we were not getting off this sofa. She jumped up and called me to come after her to the kitchen, that she was going to help get the food on the table. John told her that we were going to eat in the living room, buffet style. Mom turned and then gave this look around our living room, with a face that was saying "You want *me*…to eat…*here*…really?" Andrew and the girls jumped up and ran behind her telling her they'd help her get the food ready. My mom looked at me…Urgh. I felt like I was eight years old and in BIG trouble. I grabbed my cell phone and made motion to John to "call me". I figured since I had been doing so well lately, I would be OK going into the kitchen for ten minutes while we got the food ready. I was so confident in fact that I slipped my cell phone into my pants pocket. I started moving in warp speed, got out the salad makings, lettuce, tomatoes, onions, croutons, salad dressing, cheese all in one arm. Got the bread and butter in the other arm. The minute I turned around, there she was. About one foot in front of me. That look on her face. She started relieving my arms of everything I was carrying and setting it on the counter. I felt like a little kid. She's always had that way of making me feel "incapable". Oddest thing.

Mom: "OK Denise, we can talk now. I can tell something is up, so don't even try to hide anything from me. What's going on? Are you and the kids OK? What has John done? You can tell me..."

I felt it. The flood. The heat. The anger. The disappointment. It began to flow back into my veins. Looking at my mom, I knew she would understand, how John had treated me over the last ten years. I knew she would agree and sympathize with me. I knew she would get it. I got a flash of the cell phone on the ledge outside the shower, John telling me stories of how we fell in love. I started to reach for my cell phone, I had to call him, but my mom grabbed my arm.

Mom: "Denise, tell me what he's done to you!"

The words came soooooo slowly.

Me: "He's neglected me, for ten years..."

I stopped. The words sounded so strange. They made me frown. Something about that didn't sound right. That was wrong.

Me: "Wait, I mean, no not neglect...I don't know..."

Mom: "Oh it's OK, I think I know what's been going on, I've always thought he was a selfish oaf incapable of loving anyone but himself!"

I was horrified looking at my mom. She just said something horrible about John. She's *always* thought that…about him? I quickly got my cell phone and pressed the speed dial button to John. My mom tried to grab the phone out of my hand which made me turn quickly away from her, dropping what salad makings I had left in my arms. Baby cherry tomatoes went flying at her. Like little red missiles. John answered, all I could say was "I need you" before my mom made an incredible offensive play. She grabbed the phone from behind, yanking a wad of my hair as she swiftly took control of my cell phone.

Me: "Mom what are you doing!"

Mom: "Look, I see what's going on here. He's controlling you. Brainwashing you. You need to get away from him."

That made me think for half a second. Huh? Who's controlling who? My mom has always tried to control every situation in her life. She's the one trying to control this situation, not John. Right? My brain was starting to let the fog in. It was really difficult to try to keep the channels open. At that moment, John came bounding into the kitchen.

John: "Hellllloooo ladies, how's dinner lookin'?"
Oh. There were some serious and intense crickets at that moment. John surveyed the red tomato missiles on the floor. He looked at my mom, holding lettuce in one hand and my cell phone in the other hand (John's voice coming out of it in stereo, as she never hung up) with one strand of her hair out of place, like a one-strand-comb-over across her forehead. Very Trump-esque. Me, tensely clutching the baguette, wide-eyed, afraid

to move. Not wanting to let the flow of any more hatred or fog seep in. It seemed like the three of us stood there for 20 minutes looking back and forth at each other. Wondering who would make the next move. Of course it was my mom.

Mom: "John, Denise said you have neglected her and the children, and I want to take her and the children to live with us for a while."

I was freaking out needless to say. I was caught between believing that she was right, and knowing she was wrong. My mother is a difficult power to resist.

John: "Look Barb, you don't know what you're talking about. Denise isn't going to live with you, and the kids aren't either. You need to stay out of our marriage."

Oh, you don't even know. To see John standing up to my mom. It was so hot yet so frightening at the same time. I felt both intense love and intense hatred for him all at once. Then, words I had no control over came out of my mouth.

Me: "Don't you dare speak to my mother that way!"

The minute I said that, my eyes widened and my jaw dropped. I clutched my heart, dropping the baguette. What was I saying? My mother looked so pleased.

Me: "I mean, John is right Mom! You need to leave us alone I love John!"

My mom's face went from a smile to an immediate frown as she dropped the lettuce, clutching her heart.

Mom: "I know what this is, it's the Stockholm syndrome! I will help you Denise. You need to get away from John ASAP. He's keeping you against your will!"

Now it was John's turn to look shocked. Actually we all looked pretty shocked. Food all over the floor. John still speaking in stereo on the cell phone my mom was holding. I was slightly shaking. Too many emotions, so back and forth. I could feel the hatred for John and at the same time I was still in touch with my love for him. My own internal civil war. Which side would lose?

I felt this whooshing feeling. Like I was being pulled backwards. I gave into it. I wanted to be anywhere else instead of where I was. In a kitchen confronted by my angry mother. I kept traveling, until…I…was in a dimly lit room, with candles all around and about 15 picture frames set up on a table. I was sitting facing another velvet armless chair with Chris Harrison sitting in it.

Chris: "Denise, you have some pretty big choices to make tonight. I know this hasn't been an easy week for you, lots of emotional ups and downs. All you can do is believe in the process and hope at the end of all this, you walk away with what you came for."

He grabbed my hands and gave them a squeeze.

Chris: "I'll tell the guys you'll be out in a few minutes. Take your time. The decisions you make will affect the rest of your life."

Me: "Chris, can I ask you one question?"
Chris: "Of course."

Me: "Which one would you choose? Which guy would you spend the rest of your life with?"

Chris gave me the strangest look. He patted my hands again and stood up.

Chris: "That's why you're here Denise. You are making that choice. That's the one question I cannot answer. But I think you already know."

Chris smiled then walked out. I got up and went over to the pictures. Oddly, they were all pictures of John. Wearing different shirts, but they were all John. They were different versions of John though. I could tell there were strange Johns. Dangerous Johns. Johns that would hurt me. Johns that I wouldn't be happy with. I had to find the one. The holy grail. I had to choose wisely. I began to sweat a bit. Fearful I would choose wrong. There were beautiful frames. Some looked centuries old, made of gold with incredible detail. Some with silver with jewels inlaid in the frame. Some were wooden with gorgeous carved detail. But one frame stood out among the rest. It was a simple wooden frame with many scratches and dents in the wood. In that frame, the photo of John looked different from the rest to me. I noticed a look in the eyes of the John in the simple frame. The smallest glint of love and long lasting happiness. I started to reach for the picture frame…

John grabbed my arm and I was being yanked from the kitchen. We were running. Traveling through the fog, back to the here and now. Clouds rushing past. Moving so quickly. I tripped over the microwave cord that was plugged into the extension cord that went into the wall. The microwave crashed down behind me. I was on the ground flat. John dragged me by my arms the rest of the way to the love seat. He set my arms and upper body onto the love seat. It took me a few minutes to get my head together. I laid there, my legs on the living room carpet. My arms and torso flopped onto the love seat. It felt good. It's so comforting to know what you want in life. To not be lost and floundering. I closed my eyes and saw John. It made me smile. I took a deep, long breath. Everything was OK. I was back. In control. I finally got up and sat on the love seat. When I looked up, my mom and dad were sitting there, just staring at me. Talk about your awkward situations. I glanced at John. Wha?? LOL! He was actually trying to suppress laughter. I hadn't exactly seen any humor in this situation. Until…maybe…now? Suddenly, I too was trying to suppress laughter. Really, anyone knows, that the first rule to not laughing is to NOT try to suppress it. Anything becomes 100 times funnier if you try to suppress it. First rule of comedy. Straight out of the "Comedy for Dummies" book. DON'T suppress. Like, anything, literally ANYthing becomes hysterical in church for that very reason. There IS no laughing in church, therefore every tiny thing becomes funny. Especially if you're kneeling. Then humor is intensified by 1000. Kneeling is a good time to check out the people in front of you. Stains on their clothes, flakes in their hair, butts. I checked out a lot of butts during my church days.

There was no restraint. No control. None. At all. John and I exploded in ridiculous wonderful laughter. I pointed at the microwave on the ground. We exploded again! John pointed at my mom still holding my cell phone. LOL, I don't think I've ever laughed that hard. Suddenly my dad began chuckling. That sent John and I off again! The kids were laughing. Only odd man out in the room was my mom. Sitting there, with that angry look on her face. The face of not knowing, not understanding and not wanting to. The look of not getting her way. God she was pissed! The frown lines on her forehead looked like they were half an inch deep! I smiled at her. Hoping to soften those trenches in her forehead. Then I looked at John. How I loved this man.

Dad: "Look you all, it was good seeing you. I think I'm going to take your mom out to dinner. It's getting late anyway, who wants to cook? We love you guys."

Our laughter had died down. Awww I love my dad. He winked at me. He got it. He knew. He grabbed my mom's arm and took the cell phone from her hand and gave it to me. He stood her up, kissed her on the cheek and told her they were leaving then somewhat pushed her to the front door.

Dad: "Bye all, we love you. Hang in there, hope to see you soon."

He took my mom's arm and waved it at us. She looked too stunned to speak. The front door closed.

Andrew: "He waved her arm for her."

Andrew started laughing, then the girls, then John and I. Our house was warm, happy and filled with laughter. Like George Bailey's home in the last scene of *It's a Wonderful Life*. Perfect. We kissed the kids good night and they went upstairs to bed. I fell asleep that night, my head on John's lap, with the image of my dad manually waving my mother's arm for her. *Zzzzzzz*.

As I was falling asleep, I purposely tried to remember the hate. I don't know why, but I wanted to feel it. I wanted to be able to laugh at it, to be in charge of it. I wanted to taunt it, with my new found strength. It had such a hold of me. It consumed me. I feel…ashamed in a way, that I let it get the best of me. It happened so gradually. I think of friends of mine who have gotten divorces…and I wonder…had they found a magical little love seat, could that have changed the course of their marriages too? Why us? Why did I get lost in Los Angeles, stumble into a store that I can't seem to find again, and end up with a small, ugly love seat, that has literally saved our marriage? I think this has to be one of those things in life where you say, "Only in Los Angeles." I'm telling you, there are some very mystical and magical things going on in this town.

I'm astounded at how cruel hate is. I've said throughout my life, "Oh I hate mayonnaise and caramel, and marshmallows!" (Is now a good time to say that I have a "goo factor" as I fondly call it? Anything that is gooey or sticky gives me chills. Actual chills on my arms. Making peanut butter & jelly sandwiches, if the jelly or peanut butter get on me, I have to stop mid sandwich-ing and go wash my hands. Sooooo...I am washing my hands between 6-8 times just to make the kids school sandwiches. I am a "goo hater". I have "goo-phobia". Sounds like a real thing right?)

But, hating goo, and the kind of hate that was inside me towards John, two totally different birds. I think of friends who have gotten divorced...I never understood how they went from best friends, lovers, parents, to pure hatred. Despising each other so intensely, they lived every day shaking with hatred, just waiting to rid themselves of the other person. I was there. I felt it. But somehow, my hate got dispelled. It has left me. My body is free from that overwhelming sensation that blinded me to seeing the one I love.

I just wanted it to come to me, for just one minute, so I could give it a nice big swift kick in the ass and send it back to where it came from. Hate was scared of me now. It didn't show up. It knew it had no hold over me now. I opened my eyes once more before I completely fell asleep. I looked at the material under John's leg. The love seat. This funny little amazing love seat.

Another treat that occurred over the holiday break was Molly's birthday party. It really took some serious planning. We thought about taking the love seat outside so the kids could run around. I mean, seven year olds need to run around, and I'd prefer them not to run around in our house. But wouldn't you know, the ONE cold spell during the whole year happens on Molly's birthday weekend. IT WAS FORTY-NINE DEGREES IN LOS ANGELES! We kept our house heater on 78 during the day. (Shhhh don't tell the environmentalists.) I'm sorry, but we have thinner skin in L.A. Our blood is used to being warm. We are close to death when the temperature drops into the forties. And we are pretty much dead if the temperature reaches freezing. We don't know how to handle it. Truly. It rains…and everyone just crashes into each other. No one knows how to stop their cars. Our feet are frozen and unable to press down on the brakes. We see water on the street before us, and we panic. Not just heart racing normal panic either. I'm talking we are in such body stiffening terror that we just steer our cars into other cars just to make the horror stop. The sheer shock of seeing water falling from the sky, knowing your final hour has arrived, knowing this is alien matter falling down onto us, acid that will seep into our brains and make us do the bidding of the aliens above, it's just too much. We can't handle weather. Earthquakes, we are cool with. Meh, the ground shakes a little, and we just turn the news on to get a look at the "seismo-cam" and carry on with our days. But RAIN. That is some serious foreign, life-altering stuff there! And rain combined with cold temperatures, forget it. My advice to tourists? Don't get on the road in Los Angeles when it rains. You just don't have the defensive abilities to be able to dodge every single car that steers into you seeking an end to the madness. See, in Los Angles, we feel that if we turn our car towards another car, that other car will somehow help us. Come to our aid. "Help me Ford Focus, I'm fishtailing out of control, let me crash into your side, save me from this slick alien liquid, put an end to my water logged misery." I only wish I were being dramatic. Ask anyone who lives here. Los Angeles people are clueless when there's water on the ground. Unless the temperature is above 80, with thick smog in the air, watch out. We don't know what we're doing behind the wheel.

So the gods decided to make Molly's birthday weekend the coldest weekend of the year, which means indoor party. John thought it would probably be better. No worries about moving the love seat to a different location. "We'll just plan the party around us," he kept saying. That was his "hashtag". He kept singing this jingle he made up, like he was the marketing company for Party City. "We'lllll just, plan the party...AROUNNNDDDDDDD usssssssss". I have to admit it was pretty catchy too. Suddenly, John has become so funny to me. :) He's been making everything into a hashtag lately and it gets me every time.

I got the Oriental Trading Company catalog and went to town. John made a list of all the party food. John isn't a "chef", but as you'll remember from his "bloody pasta", sometimes he just gets "inspired". For Molly's party he wanted to do a *So You Think You Can Dance* theme. Molly watches it sometimes. She thinks

149

it's so hilarious when dancers fall down or injure themselves. Don't look at me! This is a seven year old we are talking about. Adults trying to be graceful falling down is amusing I guess.

John decided to have "Cat cookies" (a bunch of sparkles on them and "long blond hair" coming off the sides, which is really yellow gummy string things), "Paula Potatoes" (potatoes, cheese and more cheese), and "Nigel Nuggets" (tofu fake chicken nuggets). We set up a karaoke machine in the living room. We had the brilliant idea to have the girls sing as others danced. We got songs together for the girls to use for the dancers initial "auditions" and then a few songs for "Vegas Week". They would compete in teams, one dancer and one singer. Obviously everyone will make it through to Vegas Week, because that would be really cruel to dismiss a seven year old at a birthday party. Although...there is ONE little girl I'd like to not allow through to Vegas Week. Blech, can't wait until Molly sees that little slut Andrea for what she is. OH god. Did I just call a seven year old a slut? Look, here's the deal. I can spot a slut a mile a way. Whether she's 48, 24 or seven. Slutty behavior just rears it's head and there's no denying it. This kid, I swear, hits on Andrew. Andrew is oblivious. Well, Andrew is oblivious to anything female actually. Yeah. Uhhhh, I think that's probably our doing. I don't think Andrew wants to have any sort of girl in his life...for maybe...thirty years? Priest? Monk? Eeek.

Anyway, what parent lets their seven year old out of the house wearing booty shorts with her ass cheek showing? Right? Well, apparently, (according to Molly) Andrea's parents told her to take the shorts off before she left the house, and Andrea pitched a fit that that replicated an all out war. The kid screamed, hit both her parents, threw a phone through a window, took a knife to the dining room table and dug the numbers 666 into it (I might be kidding about that one), dumped sour cream in her parents bed, hid the dog in the washing machine, replaced all her moms eye shadow with paint, and wrote "JERK" in sharpie on her sleeping baby brother's forehead. Well, that's what Molly told me. Sounds pretty far fetched...but still! I'm telling you, this Andrea is just pure ick! Ick to the 9th power. (That was me getting mathematical on you)

She's just one of those bratty kids. You ask her to do something, put her plate in the trash, no, she won't do it. She always has to take the contrary position. Just when you think you have her mastered, that you will use reverse psychology and tell her "leave your plate there on the sofa Andrea", she'll just look at you smile that snotty-ass smile and then slowly place her plate on the sofa. Grrrrr!

Thinking of Andrea made me have a "Willie Wonka" type fantasy. Molly's birthday party would be the perfect "cover" for an "Andrea accident". Muhahaha. Since it's a *So You Think You Can Dance* birthday party, it only makes sense that Twitch is at our house. Now that fellow can move! So...he's introducing the girls, one by one…and when he hands Andrea the mic for her to sing, it gives her a little jolt, enough to make her singed hair stick straight up and to get those burned black marks on her cheeks. Urgh, you think I'm horrible now for having mean fantasies about a seven year old. Well just you wait, until you encounter an "Andrea" in your life. A mean, nasty, bratty little specimen with no regard for anyone, or any rules, with her butt cheeks sticking out of her shorts. What sort of an adult will this kid make? A total skank mom that's who! A skank mom having an affair with one of the dads in her kid's class.

Molly's party was great fun! We realized that seven year olds tend to make up lyrics to songs, even if the Karaoke machine is telling them the correct words, right in front of them. The singers just look out into the audience and make up their own words. It seemed to throw off the dancers unfortunately. The dancers would be in the middle of their lyrical performance and double over and drop to the ground in a full laugh attack. Aria was singing "Girls Just Want To Have Fun" and it went something like this:

Aria : *The phone rings, in the middle of dinner,*
My father yells what are you going to do with your wife.
OH daddy dear, you know you're still a son,
But girls they want to have fun,
…and squirrels.

I really don't know where she got the squirrels from, but it seemed to become more of a game after Aria went, see who can mangle the lyrics the best…or worst as the case may be. Our kids have grown up listening to 80's music, so they know it all. It's pretty amusing to see kids who come from "country" homes or "Neil Diamond" homes step into our 80's playground. Little Olivia had to sing "Rio" by Duran Duran, which... she had never heard in her life. We were on the floor with her version:

Olivia: *Moving on floor now Brian you're a bird in a pair of dice,*

Cherry pie on your face, I suppose it's very nice

Step out our door and sick your dog on your neighbor,

You know your something special and you look really ugly.

No one was even watching Kendall, as she pirouetted around the dining room table.

John and I promised each other we'd only have karaoke/dance birthday parties from now on. Even adult karaoke/dance parties, after many drinks, would be awesome. John said "Hashtag #drunkSoYouThinkYouCanDanceParties FTW!"

Then...it was Andrea's turn to sing while Hailey danced. Urgh. Barf. That kid I swear. Hailey said she didn't care what Andrea sang, she could dance to anything. Lol, kids. So Andrea stands up and John hands her the mic. She immediately tosses it back at him, hits him in the head and makes a huge THUD sound through the amplifier. We all just looked at her, like WTF! I swear, I'm going to swear at her one day. Just look her square in the eyes and say "What the fuck are you doing!? You are so FUCKING rude!" Just wait.

I will. I don't know what will happen. Is it against the law to swear at kids? I hope not because this WILL happen. A couple of the girls giggled when she threw the mic at John, which of course only encouraged her. Molly picked up the mic and handed it to Andrea. WHY DOES MOLLY LIKE THIS KID! So frustrating. So John tells her "OK Andrea, you're going to sing "Who Can it be Now' OK?" Andrea said "OK" so John starts the music. Hailey starts dancing up and over the chairs, doing high kicks in between them. Out of nowhere Andrea stops singing and says she refuses to sing "Who Can it Be Now," complaining that it's a stupid song and she wants something different. John knew better and told her to pick her own song. She sat there at the karaoke machine fiddling with it until FINALLY she starts playing "Safety Dance." Hailey had been dancing the entire time to no music. Definitely a kid in her own little world. But a peaceful, dance-y world, unlike miss nasty pants.

It was so bizarre. The whole song, she put John down. She's so evil. I mean she hates everyone equally, but, John really got the brunt of her hatred during Safety Dance solo. It wasn't a safe dance at all. It was a hateful mean dance. She was like a stand up comic all of a sudden, at a roast, just being purposely mean and snarky to John.

Andrea: *We can dance if we want to…except your dad Molly, he can't*

We can leave your friends behind…and your dad is WAY behind

Cause your friends don't dance and if they don't dance

Well they're no friends of mine...especially your dad, he's not my friend,

I say we can go where we want to, but your dad never goes anywhere...he stays on that stupid sofa...

A place they will never find, and act like we come from out of this world...

Like Molly's dad he's an alien, leave the real one far behind, and we can dance...

Then she tossed down the mic and came over and jumped on the love seat between John and I and started dancing/jumping between us! The NERVE of this child! She stepped on our thighs in the process, not much room to dance on this thing! But, wouldn't you know it, as Andrea was jumping up and down, as suddenly as she started, she stopped jumping, and plopped down between us, looked at me, looked at John, then suddenly puts her arms around both our necks, pulled us in real close and just held us there cheek to cheek. Darn love seat making me think this little girl is actually kind of sweet. But, it didn't last very long. The other little girls pulled her up and shoved the mic back in her hand wanting her to finish her song putting John down. Great. Interesting though, little skanky Andrea got up...and finished the Safety Dance singing all the lyrics perfectly. She actually sat in a chair against the wall, and encouraged everyone to watch Hailey as she danced. I looked down to the sofa shaking my head. Incredible. So little Andrea found herself moving onto Vegas Week after all. ☺

Life is going well on the love seat. We are figuring out how to live day-to-day life. How to plan parties and family gatherings. But, I do have fear in the back of my mind...constantly...about a time when we will need to leave the house. I'm sure we can't stay here forever. I mean, we're still young. I want to travel. I don't want all our kids to have to get married here, in this living room, with their parents sitting on this love seat. I want to be at the hospital when my grandchildren are born. I want to sit at the ocean again. But...I also want to love John forever. I'm looking at him now. He's a beautiful man. Something about him, that I don't think the rest of the world sees. I think that's how love works. That you alone see that special something about the person you are meant to be with. No one else can see it. Even if you told them it was there, told them what to look for. Impossible. Love is...seeing what it is they keep hidden from everyone else in the world ...except you. John has a warmth that I physically see. It radiates from him. It makes it's way to me and I feel it as it enters my soul. It ties me to him. I'm sure it was there when I hated him, trying to make its way to me, but surely I must have had some sort of block that prevented it from getting to me. Maybe hatred blocks what you are supposed to see. I'm sure it does. Hatred is so deep and evil.

I really hope that people who have been married for a while, who think it's over, who feel they have nothing left with their spouse, no love, no warmth, no sex, no humor, nothing in common...I truly hope those people get the chance we did. I hope they get the ability to step back, and see through the hate, and see if there is still love at the center their universe. I bet you, many many times people get divorced because they just get caught up in the hate. It's SO easy to do so. I was at a place I couldn't have told you ONE good thing about John. Now look at him. Sexy devil. Meow.

John: "What honey?"

Me: "What? Did I just say that out loud?"

John: "Yes...you just meowed at me."

John smiled at me and pulled my face to his. We kissed, on our little space in the world. The bit of material and padding that we call home. The cushions that gave us each other back. I love this damn love seat.

John, January 4th

I just kissed Denise. And now she's back typing on her computer. I can't help but smile. She's a spectacular woman. Just look at her. Her skin, her hair, her smile. I don't care if she's 40 or 80, I will always see her as I see her in my head. Denise. Her essence. The woman I love. No wrinkles. No age. No sagging. No age spots. MY Denise. Mine. The woman I made mine. It's like I wear glasses that when I look at her she always looks the same. I still see the Denise on our wedding day. I wonder if this is how it is for all men. No one tells you that's what love is. That the person you're with may age physically but never in your mind. I think that's one of the mysteries of love. One of the things you have to find out on your own, not be told. Because let's face it, you'd never believe that.

Our society bases so much on looks. If someone told you, "When you truly find love, you will never see that person's physical flaws, you will always see them as you did on your wedding day." You wouldn't believe it. But…what I know now, is you have to get PAST that initial love. Like years past it. You also have to get past the rough times, kids, bills, jobs. You have to get beyond all that 'life crap' to understand what love is all about. When your love survives all that junk that life throws at you, then and ONLY then can you understand what longterm soul attaching love is all about.

I would venture to guess that many people never get to this place in love. It's so easy to get lured in by that initial love feeling. The excitement. The thrill. But…what most people don't know, is that type of love is not the "great" love. It's not the one you strive to feel. It's not the life lasting one. Not the "forever" one. That initial love is so fleeting. If you spend your days only trying to experience that kind, you will be sadly lacking in your life. The grass is never greener. Maybe a different shade of green, but never "greener".

I don't know how to tell Denise this, but Molly has a performance coming up in March. Molly is quite the little actress and she's landed the starring role in the school play *Annie*. I'm sure she got the role because she basically WAS an orphan for a few months there. Her brother and sister being her parents. Gah...we were about the worst parents ever during that time.

Anyway, this isn't something that we can work out. The play won't happen in our living room. We will have to leave the house. But I don't want to alarm her just yet. I want her to be happy and not worry as much as possible. Maybe I can think of a solution, before this happens. I have a few weeks. Love seat on wheels?

Denise, January 5th

Mmmm! It's a beautiful day outside. Blue skies, crisp, bit of a wind, some huge puffy clouds wafting by...we have to do it. I stand up, grab John's hand and pull him to the front door...fling it open and pull him outside. He is laughing and so am I. Within 5 seconds we are outside, in the AIR... fresh air...wind... leaves...grass...oh my god...this is heaven...sunlight on my face...BEAUTIFUL (even though I had no sunscreen on and could feel the sun cooking up more freckles in seconds)...John's hand lets mine go and I worry for half a second until I glance at his face and see him stooping to pick up a neighborhood friendly kitty...BEST DAY EVER... except...there's a piece of egg in John's goatee.

Me: "John, honey, there's some egg in your goatee...not so attractive."

I chuckle. He laughs and with one swipe gets the egg off his face. He just smiles at me and we sit down in the grass. I'm so distracted by the little things in life.

Me: "Ermmmm honey? The chunk of egg is on your wrist."

He smiles and with careful aim, squints his eyes and flicks the egg chunk into some bushes. Fantastic!

Me: "Impressive."

We both laugh.

I feel happy. I feel good. I don't feel any hatred. I feel the warmth of the sun fill my soul. I feel the kitty brush up against my legs. I feel that tiny little ant crawl over my little toe. I feel the wind carry strands of hair across my face. Every feeling, every sensation, so beautiful.

Me: "John, you look like an ugly caveman."

WHAT?!! My eyes get huge. That thought wasn't even in my head. That wasn't even me. I look at John, he looks as shocked as I do.

John: "Where did that come from?"

Me: "I have no clue…I don't know…my mouth just spoke it, I didn't even think it, I don't think you look like an ugly cave man…a sleazy business man in a strip club perhaps but not a cave man…OH MY GOD!"

John and I look at each other. John looks angry…but then, he starts contorting his face…he looks like he is struggling, like whatever he is going through is very, very difficult…then...suddenly he…laughs. My face starts to relax from it's intent frown, ever so slightly. The right corner of my mouth turns up, towards the puffy clouds. He laughs harder…my left mouth corner

160

goes up...suddenly I find myself laughing with him. Until...I slap him across the face and call him a lazy pussy pathetic bastard. At which time John grabs my hand and pulls me back into the house, all the while I am yelling obscenities at him "Pansy ass mama's boy with your dead end job and ugly beer gut hairy fucking belly..." Not my proudest moment, with our neighbor looking on in horror...wonder what she'll say next time she picks up the kids for school. Eeeek.

Safely sitting back on the sofa, contently filled up again with love I ask John, "Why do you think it affects me more than you? You never said one negative thing, you were laughing. I hate that it takes a hold of me. I want to be like you! I don't want the hatred to own me! This isn't fair!"

John says that he thinks it is because I have a more creative mind, that I am more susceptible to the effects of the world, when not on the love seat. See how sweet he is? He makes it a compliment. Love that guy. I ask him how he is able to suppress the powerful hatred that lives off the love seat?

John: "Well, I feel it coming. I know when it's trying to enter my mind. It's like a flow, like lava, and I can sense it getting stronger, and warmer. It seems to surprise you. You just seem to blurt out things."

We both laugh.

Me: "I'm sorry honey, it's true. Things just come out, you know I don't mean them. I like your hairy fucking belly." At which time I lift up his shirt and kiss that belly just to prove my point. ;)

John: "I know sweetheart, it makes me happy that you love my hairy fucking belly."

We both laugh some more.

John: "Anyway, because I feel it coming, it gives me a chance to combat it. To try and reign it in, to get control of it. It's NOT easy. It takes every bit of concentration I have. But I seem to be able to do it, at least for a bit."

Me: "Were you close to saying anything rude to me?"

John: "I don't think so, I was actually concerned about our neighbor knowing that I had a 'hairy fucking belly'."

John kisses me.

Me: "Well, if I can do what you do, if I can learn to control it, then we can actually spend some time outside…but…you can. John. You can go to the market, you can actually do things. You can take short trips. JOHN! It's the first step! Please! You have to try! Please oh my god, go to the store! We need cream! Keep your cell phone, I'll talk to you, if things go wrong you can just come back and get on the love seat! It will be fine. We HAVE to experiment, we have to! If you are able to do this you can teach me! Maybe we don't have to live on this love seat the rest of our lives! PLEASE!!!"

John starts to say something and I am SO sure that he is going to say no that I just interrupt him…I am talking exactly 147 miles per hour.

Me: "JOHN no, you HAVE to!!! Pleesssssssssseeeeee! Oh please oh please! It will be OK I just know it will! I swear I'll talk to you the whole time...so maybe you'll have to stop occasionally to get a hold of it... concentrate... meditate... say 'Ommmmmm'...

whatever it takes! I know you can do it...you're so strong! YOU HAVE TO TRY THIS..."

At which point John puts his finger up to my mouth to "shush" me.

John: "Denise...I'll do it. I think I can do it. "

I literally FREAK OUT! I mean...FREAK OUT! I'm jumping up and down on the love seat...then I jump a little softer because I certainly don't want to hurt it.

Me: "Oh my god John! Do you even know what this means! Maybe the rest of our lives...maybe we don't have to be here! Oh my god, I'm so so excited. Oh...love seat meeting! You know I like to make lists...lets discuss every possible thing that can go wrong, and what we should do if that happens!"

John kisses my forehead.

John: "Denise, I haven't seen you this excited...in a very long time. You look really cute right now...so cute in fact...that...um...."

Me: "John, seriously! Honey! NO! There is time for 'love seat action' later! This is HUGE! We may be able to get off this thing and go out in the world! How can you think of sex right now!"

John: "Well look at you…how can I NOT think of sex? And…what is this 'love seat action' you speak of…sounds intriguing…"

John laughs and even though I don't want to, I finally break and laugh also. Grrrrrr! Hate when he does that. Ok no, actually I love it, but still!

Me: "FOCUS!!!!!"

I get my pad and pen and start to think about everything that could go wrong, things we might need to consider before he walks out that door.

Me: "John, I'm feeling faint! This is so exciting!"

John: "I know honey, it really is, very exciting"

John smiles at me, and I have to admit, when he does, "love seat action"crosses my mind. Mmmmm…what is it about him now??? He's so confident, so sure of himself. Like he could just take my hand, lead me to the bedroom…well, wait. Make that, take my hand…and sit me down on the love seat…that we were already sitting on…hmmm. Anyway, he's pretty dreamy lately. Sigh. :)

Me: "OK. Obviously if you get out of control and have a full on 'I hate Denise attack', what do we do? Do I come and get you?"

John: "No. That's not a good idea. Hmm. What if, I go with someone else? So that person has to drive me back home? I won't have a choice?"

Me: "Well, that's a good idea, but who? Who are you going to get to suddenly drive you to the market for cream that semi-understands our situation? If you start spewing 'Denise you ignorant bitch' into the phone...who will understand that?"

John: "Your dad would."

Hmmmm. I think about that for a second. Only problem is that my mother usually comes with my dad, they are a package deal. Dad would do it though, he's such a great guy, and I sort of got the impression Dad knew something was up with the love seat, that we needed to be on it for some reason. Hmm.

Me: "That just might work. Would we tell my dad a bit more about the situation? So he'd be fully onboard? I mean, I REALLY don't want my mom knowing though."

John: "I think we could tell him the basics and he would want to help us, you know?"

That makes me smile.

Me: "Yea, he's a good guy. OK, so if my dad takes you, that eliminates any possibility that you wouldn't come home. Like get all mad at me and just drive off. You couldn't because he's driving. Ok, this is good. I like it. What happens if you lose it in the store, and start screaming obscenities into the phone at me, and the store manager comes to you and asks you to stop but you won't hear of it and you punch him in the gut and he gets the wind knocked out of him then he throws up in aisle four, but everyone is so scared that no one will do a clean up in aisle four..."

John does the finger to the lips thing again.

John: "Honey...I really think it will be ok. I'm going to get ONE item. Only cream. I truly believe I can suppress it that long. And if I'm hating you on the car ride back, well, your dad will understand. I'll come in, sit on the love seat and everything will be fine. Then, we'll have the biggest best cup of coffee ever. I promise."

I breathe, I think for the first time since this thought came into my head. Huge sigh.

Me: "Then…I should call my dad?"

John: "Then…you should call your dad."

I call my dad, and tell him to go in a room where my mom can't hear. If my mom hears only my dad's side of this conversation, it could sabotage this whole plan. My mom would have the divorce attorney here in 4 minutes flat!

I am pretty direct because I just want to get going. I REALLY am anxious to see if this is going to work.

I tell my dad that John and I had been having problems in our marriage for a very long time, that we were on the verge of divorce, but that for some reason, when we are on this love seat, we are in love and the world is right. I tell him I can't explain it, so don't ask. I tell him to please just accept it, that's the way it is.

I explain that John is better than I at being able to control the hatred and so we've devised this experiment to see if we can hopefully learn to contain it and eventually have a life OFF of this love seat. My dad listens to everything, then he says "Denise, whatever you need I'm happy to do. I didn't even need that whole big explanation. I saw that you guys were living on that tiny sofa. I don't care about anything, I just want you to be happy honey."

Awwwwww! My dad. What a guy. He makes me a wee bit teary with that. I love people in this world who are just accepting. Who don't question...if it's your looks, your religion, who you're attracted to...the true angels in this world. That's my dad. :) The only downside is that there was no way my mom wasn't coming over to see the kids, but, I figured as long as I remained on the love seat, all would be well.

Me: "OK John, we are doing this! You are going to buy cream!"

John: "Never in my life have I been this excited to go buy cream."

We both laugh and hold hands until my parents get here. I look at him. What I feel, it is so so strong, I feel completely confident in my ability to talk to him, to be the "cream anchor" and keep his hatred under control.

Me: "We can do this."

John: "Of course we can ya goof ball."

He reaches over and messes up my hair like I am five years old. I'm laughing and reach over to mess his hair up, and stop short of his sparsely-haired head...and let out a "Doh!" We laugh.

Mom and Dad get to the house and Dad pretty much whisks John out the front door. I would prefer a bit more time to prepare. I guess I would have preferred to talk to Dad before he goes off with John. I want to go over all possible scenarios, but hmm, then again, with Mom there that isn't exactly possible. Well, doesn't matter. He's buying cream and coming home. There really isn't anything that can go wrong. At this point I reach over and knock on the night stand next to the love seat. Just in case. :)

My mom is in rare form. Any time she gets me alone without John, it always just sets her off. I can see on her face, she is SO certain that I'm unhappy with John, she can't WAIT until I move back in with her, so she can take total control of me and the children and she can be my "mommy" again. Tell me everything to do. Urgh. My mama. As soon as the kids are done visiting with her and run off to do their homework I know it is coming.

Mom: "Ok honey, we can talk now, tell me are you happy? You don't look happy. I was here for Christmas and you were on that couch. I come back and you're still on that couch."

Me: "It's a love seat mom, not a full sized 'couch'."

I don't know why I have to be contrary with my mom, but ANY time I have a chance to disagree with her, or point out that she may be wrong in some way, I just can't help myself. I have zero self-control. Oops.

Mom: "Honey, what does it matter? And that is a couch. I know. I have a friend, Tom, you know Tom and Lauren? Used to be clients of mine, they're good friends now. He owns a furniture factory downtown, I've been there, toured the whole facility, I should know. It's a couch. Anyway honey, tell me, what's he doing to you?"

Me: "Doing to me? What? Oh just a second Mom."

John is texting me!

John TEXT: "Honey, everything is fine, we are driving to the market, your dad is awesome."

Me TEXT: "Awwww! OMG John! Tell my dad you'll need to text me, you might need to call if it gets bad, but tell him you can't carry on a conversation with him, so I can talk to you! This is the GREATEST day ever! Well, I mean we've had a lot of great days. So many great, amazing and hysterical memories. Do you remember when you bought me that bike? Because you wanted to start biking again?"

Mom: "He's verbally abusing you isn't he, he's trying to suppress you. I can see it in your eyes. He's not letting you live the life you want."

Me: "Oh my god mom! That is so far from the truth!"

John TEXT: "LOL yes I remember the bike honey."

Mom: "Pffft. Denise. I'm your mother. You can't sit there and tell me nothing is wrong. You don't move from the sofa! Is he keeping you as a slave? Does he ever let you out of the house? Does he let you sleep in the bed?"

Her eyes squint, she is thinking very hard.

Mom: "Does he want you to wear a burka?"

Me: "Mom! Slave? BURKA??? Are you kidding me? Seriously? You think I'm John's slave? As in what? Sex slave? Mom, oh my god!"

John TEXT: "I made you ride three miles with the brake against the tire, you didn't know why your thighs were burning so bad lol"

169

Me TEXT: "omg John, my mom thinks I'm your sex slave!"

Mom: "Well I don't know about sex slave, but I've seen those horrible men on…hmm I think it was *Dateline*, those men that keep their wives in closets."

Me: "Mom, seriously? What are you talking about! 'Men who keep their wives in closets'! ??? Mom, Look at me! I'm not in a closet, I'm happy, sitting here in front of you!"

John TEXT: "WTF DENISE! Why does she think you're my sex slave! Omg…suddenly your mom has the BEST ideas! jk! hahahahahahahahah."

Mom: "I'm sure he'd let you out if he knew I was coming over, of course you're not going to be in the closet when I come over. We can't exactly sit and chat in a closet now can we Denise? Honey, I just want you to be honest with me, I can tell something isn't right. I'm very perceptive like that."

Urgh. I roll my eyes at my mom's perceived perception.

Me Text: "ha ha, mmhmm, laugh it up funny man! What is happening! Are you there yet???? TELL ME!!!!!"

Me: "Mom, for the four hundredth time, there is nothing wrong between John and I, we are totally and completely…in love!"

I can see my mom's physical reaction to my statement. Her nose crinkles, her hands clench, and she starts blinking rapidly. Boy, she sure does hate John.

John Text: "Honey, we just got here, I'm feeling a bit shaky, but I'm OK. I still LOVE YOU! :)"

Mom: "I just get the sense deep inside, you are unhappy. The kids are unhappy. They need to have happy childhoods...I could help with that..."

My jaw drops at my mom's statement. How DARE she! OMG! But I have to text John back, "feeling shaky" ...uh oh! I don't like the sound of that!

Me Text: "John! What do you mean 'shaky'!!! Are you OK?? Please tell me if you're not OK!!"

Mom: "If you need time to figure out your relationship with John, I can take the children with me, at least they can be happy."

Me: "MOM PLEASE STOP! That is so ridiculous! You are ridiculous! The kids aren't coming to live with you. You are not listening to me. I am HAPPY!"

I realize that when I say that, my face is filled with rage towards my mom.

Mom: "You don't look so happy."

John Text: "Just feeling a little funny, but have cream! Yay cream! Cream for my sex slave! hahahaha"

I laugh at John's text, but still have an angry look on my face talking to my mom. Is that even possible?

Me: "I AM happy!" I snap at my mom.

Me Text: "Ok, keep texting me! Is Dad there?"

Mom takes my hands in hers.

Mom: "Honey, look at me..."

Me: "NO MOM!" I yank my hands back. My phone drops on the floor. My mom goes to pick it up at the same time I do, and we konk our heads together…hard! I am seeing stars but quickly grab my phone away from my mom's hands.

Me: "I have to text John Mom!"

Mom: "He just controls every little thing you do, doesn't he. He leaves the house and you must text him continually, my God Denise you don't even see what you've become!"

Me Text: "John, tell me, what's happening…did you leave yet? Please just come home!"

John Text: "Why don't you…just…shut the hell up."

Me: "Oh NO!!!!"

Mom: "Oh yes Denise! You need to wake up and smell the coffee."

Me: "Yes mom, coffee in the kitchen. Go. Get some."

I immediately call John, I had imagined this happening and my strategy is to sing *Stand By You* by the Pretenders to him over the phone. Just keep singing it no matter what he says. It's a song that has a lot of meaning to us. When we were dating, we had a rocky period. John still had some interest in his ex-girlfriend (why I have no idea…she was really ugly, and chunky, and had like patchy, splotchy pimply skin and hair that looked like she stuck her finger in an electric socket…yea, she was pretty much a monster.) and he actually lied to me once when she was in town and he went to see her. I broke up with him, and he pulled a total *Say Anything* and sang *I'll Stand By You* outside my window. :) I know if I sing it to him now, he'll be OK. He'll feel me and be able to make it home. Singing this into the phone with my mom here is going to be a little weird, but I don't care. I dial John's phone.

John: "Hello?"

Oh shit, I was on speaker...my dad was going to hear this...I could tell from the sound, but I didn't have time to tell John anything, he needed to hear me sing NOW!

Me: *"Oh, why you look so sad? Tears are in your eyes, come on and come to me now..."*

Mom: "I don't want coffee honey, I want you to be OK...what are you doing?"

Me: *"Don't be ashamed to cry, let me see you through, cause I've seen the dark side too..."*

John: "Denise, what the hell..."

I cut him off with my singing, I felt it would be best if he had no chance to speak, so I sang louder now.

Me: *"When the night falls on you, you don't know what to do, nothing you confess could make me love you less..."*

Mom and John are speaking at the same time to me. When people talk at the same time to me, my brain can't process it and I end up not being able to hear anything that anyone says. Gobbledy-gook!

Me; *"I'll stand by you, I'll stand by you, won't let nobody hurt you, I'll stand by you..."*

My singing voice is pretty good if I say so myself. I stop for one second to look at my mom, who looks 58 million light years beyond irritated. That makes me chuckle...then...I hear it...a crash. Brakes screeching. My dad yelling!

173

John

Everything was going so great. Denise's dad and I got to the market, accomplished the cream mission, and were back in the car. I had been feeling a bit shaky and jittery but overall OK and I didn't have any bad feelings towards Denise. We were in the car driving home, and suddenly it hit me like a ton and a half of bricks. Right in the face. I can't STAND Denise. The cells in my body fill with hatred. I see clearly how this woman has held me down my entire life. How I would be different had I married someone else. I would be more fulfilled. I would be sexually satisfied. I would be more successful. Denise is the root of my miserable life and I hate her. I start yelling at her dad.

ME: "Your daughter is the biggest mistake I've ever made! If I hadn't married her, I would have such a different life. Your little mousey, oily-haired daughter has kept me from the life I want. The life I deserve. I hate that khaki-wearing bitch!"

Denise's dad is horrified. I can see the shock on his face...and I love it! We had prepped him pretty good I guess - he just keeps driving, faster, and faster, until he takes a turn a little too quickly and hits the center median and we flip over on the side for about two seconds, then back upright. It isn't that big of a deal, we both are fine. Under normal circumstances I might have even laughed about it. It is a total *Fast and Furious* moment. Pretty pro on Denise's dad's part. But, I am in deep "despise" of my lovely oily wife, and I want her to feel pain. I pick my phone up off the floor and yell into it.

John: "Oh my god, are you OK?! You're bleeding!"

Denise's dad isn't bleeding at all. He is sitting there, just looking at me. Like I am crazy. I can hear Denise freaking out, on the phone, and it warms my heart.

Denise over the phone: "JOHN! Oh my god, is Dad OK? Please tell me! JOHN! JOHN!!!"

I can even hear my mother-in-law in the background.

Barb: "STEVE!!!!!!"

It is totally mayhem! Awesome. Except then a police car pulls up. I don't want to deal with the police. I just want to continue freaking Denise out.

The police officers come up and are talking to Steve who is out of the car now. I am still in the car on the phone trying to wreak havoc in Denise's brain.

Me: "The blood, so much blood, hang in there Steve...Stay with me... NO! Don't close your eyes..."

Denise: "I swear to God John! You answer me right now! WHAT IS GOING ON! IS DAD OK!? ARE YOU OK? JOHN PLEASE!!!!!

I can't thoroughly explain in written form...how loud and intense Denise's voice is. She is terrified...and I feel no remorse. I am so fulfilled that she is terrified. I figure one more yell on my part will tip her over the edge.

Me: "STEVE...NO!!!!!!!!"

Then I hang up on her. That should stop her heart! However, I attract the attention of everyone standing there. Steve looks both embarrassed at me yelling his name, and angry. He's a smart man, he knows exactly what I am doing to Denise. Steve...angry? Muhahaha...I'm doing good work here. Any relative of Denise's is on my shit list. And this marriage, this bland soccer mom wife I find myself married to...is number one on my list of shit!

Steve's cell phone starts ringing in the car. I pick it up and looked at it...THE SHREW! Denise's mom...I answer it and make some noises like a man trying to speak, but choking and sputtering, unable to make any intelligible words...trying to simulate pain and suffering in my voice as best as possible.

Me: "Arrrggg...uhhhhggg...AHHHHH...(choke, cough)...EHHHAHHHHHH..."

Denise's mom: "OH MY GOD STEVE TALK TO ME!!!!"

Then I hang up. I can hear Denise in the background, screaming. I know she is helpless, unable to get off that stupid love seat. I am laughing to myself as one of the police officers walks over to investigate why I was yelling Steve's name in the car.

Police Officer: "Are you alright, sir?"

Me: "Oh, yeah, I think I'm OK."

Police Officer: "You were yelling?"

Me: "Oh, yeah, just wanted to make sure my father-in-law was OK."

Police Officer: "I just want to ask you a couple of questions."

Me: "Sure, my wife is a total nagging horrible beeotch."

The police officer looks totally startled, then quickly regains composure.

Police Officer: "What does that have to do with the accident, sir?"

Me: "Well, she's such a horrible excuse of a woman, that her dad probably got distracted thinking about how he failed as a father, and crashed."

The police officer's eyebrows arc up towards the clouds.

Police Officer: "That's an exceptionally rude thing to say about your father-in-law, who just got into an accident."

Me: "Exactly!"

I smiled.

Police Officer: "Sir, can you get out of the car."

I get out of the car, sensing that this officer doesn't like me one bit. I laugh as I think about what a great "bad guy" I make. Able to get everyone to hate me with only a couple of words. Yet another talent Denise doesn't appreciate about me.

Police Officer: "Can you tell me about the accident? Speed your father-in-law was driving prior to the crash? Were there any other vehicles around? Anything on the road? Any distractions in the car?"

Me: "The only distraction in the car was my ugly, annoying wife!"

Police Officer: "Sir? She was in the car?"

He starts to look around a little alarmed.

Me: "Oh no, I was on the cell with the creature, she was singing The Pretenders' "I'll Stand by You", you know? Out of tune, I might add, sounded like Meatloaf with a cold."

Oh, I've broken him, he can't stand it any longer, he moves in a little closer to me and lowers his voice.

Police Officer: "With all due respect, sir…why are you still married if you despise her so much?"

Me: "That's a very good question, and one that I am determined to fix ASAP. I am going to the attorney tomorrow, and getting the fastest divorce EVER!"

The police officer takes a step away from me, and gives me a look up and down with utter disgust on his face. Such an ugly look, it reminds me of my blushing bride back home.

I tell the officer about the accident, it was no one's fault, Steve just took the corner a bit too sharply and we hit the center divider just right so we tipped momentarily. He seemed satisfied with my account and walked back to his partner and Steve.

Look, I could be the ultimate ass and give a story that gets Steve in trouble, but honestly, I just want to be done with these freaks that I have been married to the last fifteen years of my life. I don't want to have to go to court dates, more attorneys…I just want to be done. I want to be free from the circus. The bearded lady can even keep the kids. I don't care. I want to be free. I want to have fun. I want to date, drink, have sex, go out to dinner. I want to live my life. I don't want to die with all these regrets I have. I don't want to be one of those men stuck with the same, miserable, boring housewife for eternity. I don't want to be the old guy in a wheelchair at my 50th wedding anniversary, pretending it was all worth it...unable to have enough breath to blow out 50 candles on my heavily buttercreamed cake, dribbling drool and cake juice down my chin, looking at my wrinkled and osteoporosis ridden wife, smiling, telling everyone I'd do it again. No. I can't.

I am awakened from my 50th wedding anniversary nightmare by Barb and her evil horror daughter Carrie driving up at the same time as the tow truck. (Five second flash daydream of Denise as Carrie at the prom with blood falling all over her while everyone points and laughs.) I'm pretty shocked due to the fact that Denise can't seem to control herself once she gets off that stupid love seat, but I welcome the battle. I march over to her.

Barb: "STEVE, are you OK? OH MY GOD!!"

Denise: "DAD! You're standing! What's happening?!"

Me: "Fancy seeing you here, bimbo," I greet Denise.

Denise: "Too bad you didn't die wuss wiener mama's boy."

Steve: "Barb, Denise I'm fine! Totally fine, just a minor accident is all."

Me: "Too bad you couldn't dress in clothes other than mom jeans, you repulsive beast."

Denise: "I want to puke...on your face!"

Barb: (looking at me) "I want a divorce!!"

179

Me: "What the hell are you talking about woman, I'm not married to you! God forbid!"

Steve: "Hey, watch it John!"

Police officer: "Pardon me, I just need a bit more…"

The officer is interrupted by Denise.

Denise: "Don't you talk to my mother like that! You disgust me! Your bald head is sweating and your button over your gut is open, I can see your belly fat and hair! I want a divorce more!"

Me: "My belly fat and hair are worlds better than your swinging-in-the-breeze mom arms! And YES LET'S GET A DIVORCE ASAP! (Looking at Barb) I want a divorce from you too you ugly control freak!"

Barb gasps! Not sure whether she gasps at being called ugly or a control freak. Who cares! Steve is giving the police officers a bit more information as the tow truck readies the car. The officers are jotting things down without looking as they look back and forth between all of us as this ugly battle is unfolding before them. I glance at the tow truck driver, his mouth is open.

Barb: (In a lower voice to Denise) "See honey? You're seeing his true colors, this is the man you married. He has never made you happy and doesn't have the capability to ever do so. He is a self-centered ugly, vile, worthless shell of a man. Has no looks and can't even make a good living. Total, utter…failure!"

Steve, seeing my rage building and being the only one who can truly understand the situation, quickly opens the back door of Barb's car and shoves her in.

Steve: "Get in back Denise…NOW!"

Said with enough true 'angry dad tone' that Denise actually complies! As for me, I can't say enough to that evil bitch!

Me: "God Barb, if you only knew the things Denise says about you when you're not around! You're a monster! So in denial! You don't know how everyone around you HATES you!"

Barb isn't even listening to me. She puts her arm around Denise who is yelling things at me out the window I can't even hear. Jesus, she looks like one of those angry criminals in the back of the police cars on *COPS*.

Police officer: "Alrighty then, looks like we're done here."

The officer looks off to the car being towed away, then to the car with screeching Denise, back to me, to his partner, who gives a slight shrug, and back to Steve.

Police officer: "Ok sir, well…"(long pause………..) "Good luck then."

He shakes his head and both officers get into their patrol car as Steve grabs my elbow firmly and starts leading me to Barb's car.

Me: "OH NO! No no no! Steve, no, I cannot get in that car with *HER!*"

John says nothing, just leads me harder to the car of dread! I stop at the door to fight him and protest once more, and dear god, this man, the witch's father, has the gall, the NERVE, to slug me in my stomach! Then he gives me a swift shove into the front seat! I am gasping for air, doubled over, amazed at the strength Steve just pulled out of nowhere, when I hear the cheers from the back seat. Urgh.

Denise: "Woo! Dad! Way to go! YES! Slug him again! Lower this time please! The testicular region would be AWESOME! Come on Dad! Do it for meeee!!!!

She sounded downright gleeful! It was sickening. Then the hell boar spoke.

Barb: "Haha! Steve, didn't think you had that in you, I'm proud. Any man who has kept our daughter as a prisoner in a closet deserves to be slugged!"

Steve's eyebrows raise and he looks at me with a questioning look.

Steve: "Wha..???"

But I can't speak back. I am feeling sorry for myself, and still trying to get my breath. I don't think I've ever actually been slugged in the stomach. It's not pleasant. I was never the "testosterone-fueled angry fighter type of guy." I'm more the "hang out, quietly in the back of class, not speaking to anyone type of guy." Sigh. Denise however, can't shut her ugly trap!

I shut my eyes, and continue to hold my stomach until we arrive home.

Denise

HAHAHAHAHAHAHA! My dad. My sweet, soft spoken Daddy. The one who never speaks up for himself. The one who lets mom walk all over him.

SLUGGED JOHN IN HIS FAT, SOFT GUT! LOL! I seriously cannot stop laughing about that! It may be one of the best moments in my entire life. I am in the backseat rolling with happiness and laughter. And even when I'm done laughing, you can bet I am going to continue laughing as HARD as I possibly can just to annoy John. I have never seen John physically hurt like that, and it feels naughty to say, I really enjoyed it. As suddenly as my dad slugged John in the belly de fat, my mind wandered...

I am standing over John. Dressed REALLY hawt. In, um, well, black leather? And very high black heels. I have a whip in my hand, and a candle. No, a cigarette. NO...a flame torch! John is tied to the dining room table, the one he complains about over and over and over because I got it at Pottery Barn and not Ikea! I should explain, that first off, it was damaged, had dings out of it on two edges, so I got a REALLY great price! And secondly, we have never purchased ONE thing from Ikea that has lasted more than 8 months, because John can't put shit together! He's the most NON-HANDY handy man (I guess that would make him unhandy) in the universe! Everything that man puts together comes apart within months. So seriously getting a dining room table at Ikea would have cost us more money, as it would have fallen apart, and we would have had to buy a new dining room table. But of course the dummy doesn't understand my logic...EVER!

So he's tied to the very sturdy leg of the Pottery Barn dining room table, very nice pine. Doesn't really match any of our other furniture, but hey, like I said. It was a good deal.

John's screams are muffled by a Christmas themed dish rag I've stuffed in his mouth. I can see Frosty's lower snowball sticking out of his mouth. (Raising an eyebrow at that statement!) John is wearing his usual striped t-shirt and plaid shorts with the luscious addition of business socks. Ugh. He disgusts me. I have blindfolded him with my Frownies. (Don't judge, I don't really have S & M items around the house, a mad housewife has to be resourceful.) In case you don't know, Frownies are so great. They're little tape-y things that you peel off and put between your eyes, over your frown lines at night, so you don't get any more frown lines.

John looks so stupid with Frownies all over his eyes. Idiot. I lean down and whisper to him...

Me: "I *am* your Mrs. Robinson."

I see him shudder as I fire up the flame torch.

Me: "I'll show you fifty shades of red...on your butt..."

I yank his ugly plaid shorts down and lower the flame torch...

Steve: "We're home thank god, everyone inside NOW!"

Wow, my dad screamed. I never hear my dad yell, much less scream. It was actually a little scary. There was nowhere I wanted to be more anyway, than inside, away from all that ridiculous drama that we had just gone through. John and I get out on the same side of the car, and pause for a second as we catch each other's eye. I squint. He squints. I make the "ick" sound deep back in my throat. He spits on the ground. I roll my eyes and take a step forward but he manages to get his foot right in my path and I trip and fall to the ground. He chuckles as he turns to walk in. NO WAY! What an ass! On my hands and knees, I grab the closest thing to me, which is a sprinkler head. John was SO fucking proud of these two sprinkler heads in our front yard because he actually replaced them...and they worked! GRRRR. I rip it from the ground and hurl it at him. It clocks him right above the right ear! He falls to the side, taking like four steps to catch his balance YES! I laugh and stand up and start walking behind him. Stupid ass.

In a split second he kicks Andrew's skateboard backwards and dammit, I step right on it, and fly forward back onto the grass again! I am SO MAD! I think I'm foaming at the mouth. I'm really not kidding. I pick the skateboard up and throw it as hard as I can. My only problem is, I forget to aim at anything. It hits my mom in the butt, hard enough to cause her to fall back on it into the grass. John and I manage to make it to the front door at the same time. We both look back to see my mom sitting on the skateboard on the front lawn. Her legs are outstretched in front of her. She looks like she has no idea what just happened to her. I laugh, I can't help it. It is such a funny sight. And she isn't getting up. That makes me laugh more. My dad looks at her, and starts laughing too. I glancd at John, who is starting to smile…I feel some odd, prickly pins of heat in my neck.

John opens the door and I push him aside and go in first. I am still laughing about my mom sitting down so hard on that skateboard. When I hear John still laughing, I turn to look at him. Prickly pins again, and…it is so odd…for a split second, I feel no hatred towards him. My smile turns genuine at him, and his smile seems to turn genuine towards me. Like robots, we both walk to the love seat and sit down.

Ahhhh…here comes the warm flow. The ice melting in my veins, the warmth, light and love spreading throughout my body. I take John's hand, sit back, close my eyes, and just enjoy the sensation of all that hatred leaving me. He holds my hand so tight, until I open my eyes. He is smiling at me. Then I notice my mom, sitting about three feet from me, in a chair, her hair a bit messed up from the skateboard incident. She is just staring at me. Frowning. She glances at John, and every single time she does, she has a facial twitch. It is really odd. I just sit there, wondering how long she is going to continue this. Frowning at me, twitching at John. I don't even want to look at my dad, as I would miss a twitch. I counted eleven before my dad speaks and breaks the silence.

Dad: "Well guys, that was about the most, um…by far the…well, yeah, that was an interesting trip to the market, wasn't it?"

Wow! My mom was still twitching.

John: "Steve, I can safely say, that is a market trip I'll never forget."

Dad: "No hard feelings there John?"

Dad has a ridiculous grin on his face. John immediately starts laughing.

John: "Nope. No hard feelings. But, I have a whole new respect for your muscle tone Steve. Seriously, something to aspire to. I might need a personal trainer."

Dad starts to laugh too. He stands up and grabs my mom gently by the arm.

Dad: "Come on sweets. Time to go."

Mom's face says it all. She is still twitching. I try to think how this all looks from her perspective. Basically, it looks like John and I are clinically insane. We go from hating each other one moment, to sitting on this little love seat, and in love. Poor Mom.

Mom: "So...you're not getting a divorce?"

Awwww, she looked genuinely sad.

Me: "No mom, I think we'll be OK. It was just a weird day."

I try to give her the best most reassuring smile I can, and I grab her hand and kiss it. She holds onto my hand, not letting go. Her face is pleading with me to change my mind about John, to finally divorce him, and come back to her. Be her little girl. Let her mother me. But in that moment, I see in her eyes, she lets go. She finally lets go of her hope. She finally lets me grow up. She has finally decided to let me live my life. My dad sees it too. He puts his arm around her, kisses her

187

cheek, and they walk out the front door not saying anything else. It is a bittersweet moment for me. It's what I've always wanted…to grow up. To have my mom accept my decisions and respect them. But, I have to admit, I also have a little remorse. My mom has been controlling and in my face, in my business since before I was born. I'm not sure I know how to live fully, with my mom respecting my boundaries and accepting John. Wow. My days just keep getting more intense. And bizarre. And…good. :)

I watch the front door close and turn back to John, who is moving closer to me and smiling. He takes my hands in his. Mmm…what a feeling. To feel the sensation of the man you love take your hands, while looking into your eyes. Hand holding doesn't get enough credit. There's something extremely special about it. We do everything with our hands. They are us. Our power. Our creativity. To hold another's hands feels very meaningful and deep.

John: "Denise. Do you understand what just happened?"

He is smiling so big!

Me: "Well, my dad socked you in the gut?"

I totally laugh. But oddly, he doesn't. He just keeps smiling at me. Gah. I hate being the only one laughing.

John: "Wellllll…yes… but that's not what I mean."

Me: "You mean how the whole grocery trip went bad, and now we really are stuck here on this love seat?"

Now he laughs! Confusing man.

John: "No honey, I mean how that grocery trip showed us that we are NOT stuck here on this love seat."

I crinkle my entire face and cock my head sideways. Then I lightly sock him in the stomach.

John: "Hey now, I'm still a little sensitive."

He rubs his stomach with his hands and sticks out his bottom lip. I laugh and squint at him.

Me: "Ok...so...tell me how this means we're not stuck on this love seat...?"

John: "Well, we are not stuck on this love seat, because of what happened when we walked through that door. When your mom fell on that skateboard, we both laughed. Something funny overcame the hatred. It was more powerful than the hate we felt for each other. I know you felt it. I saw it in your eyes. We SMILED at each other Denise, BEFORE we got on the love seat. Us, laughing together...was stronger. We didn't need the love seat. I almost wanted us to not sit on it, to see what would have happened. But your parents were here, and I think they needed a little peace of mind."

I look away from John, back to the front door, thinking about what he has just said.

Me: "Hmmm...you're right. I did feel that. I did..."

John: "Soooooo...I'm not exactly sure what that means. Do we constantly have to be in a state of laughing? When we're off the love seat? That might become a bit tiring."

We both laugh.

Me: "And how do we just make ourselves laugh on command…continually, when we're off of this thing?"

I hit the cushion next to me with my fist. I look up at John and he hits his cushion with his fist. Then I hit his cushion. Then he hits my cushion. I pick up the back cushion and smack him in the head with it.

John: "Oh yeah? Well, this is me being REAL!"

He picks up his back cushion and bops me smack in the face! I instinctively get up and go behind the love seat, to get out of his reach, and I whack him in the back of his head! He stands up in front of the love seat with his cushion.

Me: "CUSHION FIGHT"!!!

At this point, the kids come downstairs and are watching us with open mouths, but we don't notice them at all.

John: "Lady, you're goin' down, downtown…to Chinatown…"

Me: "Oh yeah? Ya think so? Well, you're goin' Dittily…to Little Italy…"

That's all I need, he cocks his head in confusion at my statement, and looks sideways with his eyes for a couple of seconds to ponder what in the world that means…that I was going to send him to Little Italy? I use my cushion straight on, and shove him as hard as I can, he goes flying backwards into the chair my mom had been sitting on. He sits down hard!

I laugh so hard. He uses my moment of head tossed back laughter to take advantage of my vulnerability. He charges up and over the love seat, and tackles me with his pillow onto the ground. He pins me down with his cushion.

John: "5, 4, 3, 2, 1...YES! Ding, Ding, Ding, WINNER!"

He jumps up and raises his hands, doing a little victory jig. He spots the kids and runs over and grabs Molly and puts her on his shoulders and races through the house.

John: (Yelling) "VICTORY LAP... AHHHHH YEAA!"

Molly is laughing her head off as they run around the entire house. We are all laughing. What a great and wonderful day. :)

After the kids are in bed, we get ourselves settled on the love seat, ready to go to sleep. We are in our usual position, my legs on the inside, his on the outside, pressed tightly together. We look at each other and smile. Knowing exactly what the other is thinking.

John: "Sooooooo......"

Me: "Yeeeeessssssss....???????"

Our smiles get bigger.

John: "You realize, we had a blast, during our pillow fight, and all of it took place OFF the love seat?"

Me: "Oh yes Mr. Hughes. I do indeed realize that. I almost didn't want to verbally acknowledge it in case it wasn't real."

John smiles at me again. His look becomes different. More intense. His eyes take me. Lock. Couldn't look away if I wanted to.

John: "You're very beautiful Denise. Very…beautiful…"

I blush and try to get us back on topic. Sorry, I don't handle compliments well. Especially when there's no escaping, when you are locked eye to eye with the "compliment-OR".

Me: "Anyway, so let's talk about what this *means*…"

John: "Verrrrrrrryyyyyyyyyyyy beautiful…."

Me: "JOHN!!!!"

I was bright red by this point. He laughed a nice hearty laugh.

Me: "Laugh it up funny, funny man. You're going to need to laugh a LOT it seems."

John: "OK, OK. Let's get down to business. So, you're my secretary and I want you to take a *dictation*…"

He winks at me.

Me: "OH MY GOD JOHN!!!!!!!!!!!!!"

We both laugh so hard.

Me: "Jesus John, it's a wonder we get anything done."

John: "I know, right?"

Me: "Ok, so, now, we know, when we are on the love seat, we are good. And now we also know, that when we are OFF the love seat, but sharing funny stuff, we are good."

John: "Sharing funny stuff? Ohhh la la…kinky. I want to show you my funny stuff."

Me: "John Laurence Hughes!"

John: "Ohhhh ouch!!!!"

He grabs himself as if he were in great pain.

John: "You did not just call me what my mom calls me…arrrrgggg…it BURNS!!!!!"

I laugh at this man sharing my love seat. What in the world has happened to us? This is how John used to act when we were dating. The times we share now, the talks we have, everything is like it used to be. How is this possible? Was this always here? In us? We just let the years of marriage and routine stifle it? Camouflaged behind bills, laundry and grocery lists? Is it always still there for everyone? I think of all the divorce. All our friends who've gotten divorces, families torn apart. I wonder if it was possible for any of them to regain what they all had at the beginning of their relationships. The magical moments that attracted them to one another initially. And what about that attraction? What causes it? Is it really just hormones? Pheromones? Subconsciously picking someone that looks like your father? Is it just being in the right place at the right time? Is it being so drunk you go home with the first guy you meet? Or is it deeper than that? Is there actually something to reincarnation? Have we been with each other before? Are we always searching for our soul mate? The one we share lifetimes with? I have many questions about the universe and what makes us stay with one person for a lifetime. John breaks my concentration abruptly.

John: "HEY! Lady! Snap out of it! We have some big thinking to do here!"

He actually startles me into reality. I smile at him.

John: "I love you."

Me: "I love you John Hughes. We're going to figure this out. And we're going to get off this love seat."

John: "That we are."

He sits up and kisses me. A nice, slow, long kiss. Then he pulls back, and does the 'ol "got your nose" thing with his hand. He looks in his hand at my "nose" then gasps in shock.

John: "OH MY GOD DENISE! I didn't think that would actually work!"

I burst out laughing!

Me: "John, why do you treat me like I'm a kid!"

John laughs then turns a little serious.

John: "Because you are a kid Denise. You have the heart of a child. You play at life. It's why I love you so. Everyone rushes around. They work. They pay bills. They grow up. Your heart is so young, carefree, playful. Every time I even think about being an adult, you suck me right back to your reality. I love it. I have so much fun with you. I just...I love everything about you Denise. You make me happy."

That's it. In one instant I am up and on top of him kissing him. I turn off the light with my left hand. Oh I am such a smooth operator.

John

Alrighty. I've got some figuring to do. I think well when I'm writing, so I'm just going to put this all down on paper and see what I can come up with. So, obviously, on the love seat Denise and I are fine. As we have proven, we are actually fine off the love seat, as long as the mood is light, and we are laughing. We do not have to be laughing non-stop, as exhibited by our pillow fight. Hmmm. I wonder if other "happy" emotions would do the same. Like, say, sex? Can't blame a guy for tryin'. Lol. But honestly, I bet that would work. So if we are ok for all "happy" emotions off the love seat, potentially, we really could head out together.

I need to think of ways to keep our mood "up" at all times off the love seat. If I can manage this, Denise and I can go to Molly's play. Together. What a great evening that will be. Maybe we should take a cab, in case anything goes wrong. Then the cab will be responsible for taking us home, and not ourselves...which could end up...not so good! With this newfound knowledge, I think I need to tell Denise.

Me: "Denise?"

I look across the love seat to her there on her laptop. She's cute.

Denise: "Yes?"

Me: "We are going out, and we're going to be OK."

Denise: "OK. When?"

Me: "I love how you just jump at the chance! No fear."

Denise laughs: "Oh I have fear. I just have a bit more confidence after the pillow fight."

Me: "Well you know Molly has the play coming up. Her first starring role. I didn't want to worry you…but now I think we can do it. We can go to the play."

Denise: "Okay. I have a little fear."

Me: "No time for fear. We are going to *Annie*. Together. With Andrew and Amber. We're going to sit in the audience, and cheer her on."

Denise: "And we'll give her a huge bouquet of flowers when she's done!"

Me: "Yes!"

Denise: "Ok, we'll do it."

Uh oh. I can tell when Denise is having her daydreams. Her eyes stay open, but they slowly drift to the side and up. I never know if they're good daydreams, bad daydreams, if they're total fantasy, or based on reality. She's a special creature, my Denise.

:)

Denise

John just told me we are going to Molly's play. As a couple. A normal couple that gets to go out together. God, it's been so long since we've gone out together. Even before this whole love seat thing, well, basically we hated each other. Geez, we haven't gone out together in ages!

What if things go wrong? I mean, chances are very, very good they will go wrong. We don't know what we're doing. We don't have experience going out! Why are we choosing to go to Molly's play for our first attempt? Isn't that dumb?

My world shifts, it's a bit blurry, or maybe there's a fog machine in my head. I'm in a different room. I'm in the school multi-purpose room. I'm fidgeting in my seat, due to my close proximity to "the pig". I'm actually touching elbows with him. It disgusts me. I feel a ball of nausea bouncing around in my stomach. I notice the room slants upward. Like a theatre. I'm dressed so weird. Wow, this is not "mom attire". I have a strapless black dress on, and a black beret. I chuckle out loud at my ridiculous outfit. Ugh, John whispers in my ear, "Be quiet you ugly monster." He's so charming. I look at him with as much hatred as I can muster, but I think the effect is lessened with this stupid beret on my head. A family and their two small children move in front of us to get to their seats. The mother is holding a small child, looks about 18 months or so, holding a bottle of milk. As they slowly make their way by, the small child drops her bottle right on John's fancy black pants. LOL! Little white milk dots all over his perfect pants. I laugh so hard. I can't help it. People are 'shhhh-ing' me, but so what! What a great kid! Smart, bright, clever child! I make eye contact with the little person in her mother's arms, we share a "look" with each other. She knows what an ass John is. She dropped that bottle for me. I love that kid!

John is livid. His face is red. He is going to blow, any second. He is obviously more angry about my laughing than he is about his newly acquired milk dots. He leans over and whispers "Shut up!" I am immediately filled with both rage, contempt and a strength. I am not going to let this man treat me like this any more. Who is HE to tell me not to laugh, when he gets a little milk on his pants? What a baby! This is no strong man! This is a pussy wussy ding-dong asswipe dependent on his mama putrid man! I am so disgusted with him at this moment! I stand up, yank my stupid beret off my head and scream, "He said shut up, HE SAID SHUT UP!" John tries to pull me back down to sit in my chair, but I am not having any of it. Screw him. I WANT to embarrass him!

The fog starts rolling back over me, cooling me off, reminding me that this is just a daydream. I feel my skin prickles begin to subside. One drop of sweat rolls down the side of my neck. I blink and open my eyes to see John staring at me.

Me: "Oh, hi."

John: "Wow, that must have been a doozy."

He reaches over and wipes the drop of sweat with one finger and smiles at me.

Me: "Oh it was. I think…"

I trail off, as I realized how totally stupid what I was about to say was.

John: "Yessssss…my darling????"

He laughs. He knows exactly what is happening. I've told him about my daydreams before. He always says that I'm a person who dangerously teeters on the brink of insanity and reality. Well, he kids me about it. I don't think he really think's I'm teetering on the edge of insanity. Hmm. I hope he doesn't?

John: "Well…are you going to tell me?"

Me: "Um, OK don't laugh."

John: "Oh honey, too late for that."

As he laughs. Grrrr I roll my eyes.

Me: "We were at Molly's performance. We were not happy with each other, to say the least. You know, the usual when we're off of this thing."

I look down to the love seat and make a face at it.

Me: "See, we were, um…well…actually, we were in that 'Til Tuesday video, in the theatre, you told me to shut up, I was wearing a beret…and I stood up…"

That's all I have to say. John starts laughing so hard, he can't even hear anything else I say. He is holding his stomach, and tears start coming down his cheeks. I let out a big sigh while he has his moment, at my expense. But…then I start to think about what I just said. What I just envisioned. John and I. In the classic 80's 'Til

Tuesday video. lol Wow, I thought Amie Mann was SO cool at that time. GIRL POWER! I start to laugh with him, instead of fighting my own embarrassment. It feels GREAT!

We laugh a bit more then get down to business. We plan out everything. Every possible thing that can go wrong. We think the chances of us BOTH being flooded with hate at the exact same moment are slim. So we each have our methods to get the other one to laugh and lighten up the mood. We have the kids get us joke books. John downloads funny family videos on each of our phones, so we will have those accessible in an instant. We think of all our funniest moments together. We have lists on each of our phones, at the ready. My list is the following:

1) John sits on plastic cup at party.

2) Us gossiping about everyone during our wedding…forgetting we had mics on, and that's the reason no one has ever seen our wedding video.

3) My mom thinking I wear a burka and am John's sex slave.

4) Still not having sent out our thank you notes for our wedding…almost 14 years ago.

And how we always joke about sending them out now. lol

5) How we totally stalked Daryl from *The Walking Dead* TV show at a Peter Murphy concert.

6) When John tripped coming in from the garage, and fell, and somehow managed to travel about fifteen

feet on his stomach into the kitchen. The kids were so baffled by that. They did a total investigation, got out measuring tapes, took notes. No one understood how he traveled that far. To this day, it remains in the unsolved case files.

7) When we went out to a bar one night, got a little tipsy, then saw an alien bird walk in front of our car. It was SO weird! The bird was about 2 feet tall, had long legs. We got out of the car and followed it to someone's doorstep. We even have photos of it. OMG we have laughed about that bird. Even though we were tipsy, I swear to you, that bird is real. You don't see birds like that in LA. Something was totally up with that bird.

8) When the kids were little, I dressed up like John - suit, tie, put a pillow in my stomach for reality purposes of course. He dressed up like me, wig, lipstick, and a pink bathrobe. We totally got in character and acted like each other. We scared the shit out of our kids. We actually had to stop because apparently we were so convincing, they started crying.

9) The time at Thanksgiving my mom spilled all the scalloped potatoes in the oven, on the window part of the oven door. She was so mad, scooping those potatoes back into the glass baking dish. Then she just put more cheese on top and baked them again. We had to eat the potatoes that were oozing into the oven door. OMG we laughed about that.

10) How when I told my mom I (Catholic raised) was going to marry John (Jewish)…she cried and

asked me, "What would the blessed Mary think about this?"

11) How we were playing Pictionary with my parents, and my dad drew a total penis. (AKA basketball court?????) My mom kept guessing cucumber, telephone pole, rolling pin...and John and I couldn't even speak. We only almost had hernias by trying to suppress our laughter so hard.

12) The time we were um...having sex and my knee popped out. I was on my hands and knees (not in a kinky way either...) for about 40 minutes before I finally got myself flipped over and popped it back in myself. John tried to pop it back in for me, but he couldn't cause me pain, and it's INCREDIBLY painful to actually push my knee down and pop it back in. So there I was, in my cute little outfit, popping my own knee into place. A total sex night gone bad story.

Andrew and Amber are ready too. They each have lists of jokes, mostly about my mom, that they are ready with. Andrew fancies himself the physical comedian, so I'm quite certain he's planned some stunt falls, just in case.

John really gets creative and crops photos of my mom, close up on her face, and captions them. I don't know what they say, I guess the element of surprise will help us through this. Things are funnier if you haven't seen them before.

We have a LOT of options, many things to hopefully make us laugh and lighten the mood if things go bad. I'm nervous, but I'm really excited. I think we can do this. I want to do this, with every cell in my body. I'm desperate to do this. I want off this love seat. I want to experience life with John. He's my love. I want to travel far and wide with this man. I want to drink wine in Paris. I want to snorkel in Australia. I want to eat sushi in Japan. I want to shop in New York...all with him. This wonderful, amazing man. The love of my life. John Hughes.

Denise, One Week Later

Things have been going well. Actually planning a night out has really helped us learn how to live off of the love seat. Believe it or not, I've started doing laundry again, and I have to tell you. I don't mind it one bit. :) I'm sure in the future I'll complain about it again, but for right now, I am loving the moments off this love seat. The feeling of being free. The hope that maybe not only can life continue OFF of the love seat, but that I can be happy and fulfilled with John until the day we die. It's a very romantic thought to think of being with someone forever. Eternity...just oozes with romance. What an enticing word.

We will give ourselves time limits. I usually work in about 5-6 minute periods, John can handle more. He can be away from the love seat for about ten minutes before he needs to come back. We only need to actually be on the love seat for about five minutes, so we are spending a pretty good portion of the day now off of it. Tonight is the dress rehearsal. We are going to go off the love seat together, out in back, and try to eat dinner out there. We are going to try to be as funny as we can and keep each other laughing and amused. Our goal is two hours. We think if we can pass that amount of time, the play will be no problem at all.

Andrew is going to be monitoring us. Every 15 minutes he's going to come out and see how we are doing. If things have gone bad, he's been instructed to tug and pull and do whatever is necessary to get John back on that love seat. We figure if he can get John on the love seat, John can figure out what to do next and John is also stronger than me. If he needed to regroup on the love seat, then go get me and carry me to it, he could.

It's not a perfect plan, things can always go wrong, but better to go wrong at our own home than in front of every parent at Molly's school, all Amie Mann style, right? Right. ;)

Denise, Later than evening

Well. OK then. We had dinner. Just a nice little, quiet dinner in the backyard. I look up from my computer, out the sliding doors to the backyard. The patio is covered with food, broken glass, our patio furniture is turned over, and red, hardened candle wax is all over the ground from the candles tipping over. Looks like Axl Rose's handy work. Yea, John and I live like rock stars. lol.

Everything was fine, going quite smoothly. John is amazingly pro at keeping me laughing. He's really a funny guy! But all it took was for the kids to have problems getting the lasagna out of the oven. I told John that I should have gone and waited on the love seat, but he winked at me, so cute, and told me "Stay right there missy. I won't leave you for long." Gah...when he talks to me like that, well, it's just not something that I can resist. Makes me...

mmmmm…yea. Well. Unfortunately that feeling didn't last long.

I could feel it the minute he walked away. The tension building inside me. It starts in the stomach. Always in the stomach. A knot. Then it gets larger. A ball. Then it swirls and spins, leaving a trail of hatred molecules that make their way throughout my body. My hands and feet are the last parts of my body to feel the hatred, but eventually even my finger and toenails are filled with severe, mind pounding hatred for John.

John didn't take that long helping the kids get the lasagna out of the oven and serving it. But it was enough time. Those few moments without John, without a lightened mood, without laughter, were enough to send me off the edge into the pit of anger. I just sat there. Becoming more and more furious. Didn't move from my seat. Eventually I was shaking with anger. The second I saw him come through that sliding door holding those plates of lasagna, I picked up my salad plate and hurled it like an expert Frisbee golf player, right at him. It was so pretty. As it spun, in slow motion, each piece of lettuce waited its turn, all flying off one after another. It was so artistic. Perfect lettuce spirals in the air. The beautiful "air art" was interrupted by John's face. Ahhhh, I can't even express to you how elated I was to see Caesar dressing on John's face. It filled me with joy.

I think John was already edgy from being away from me, and also not laughing. Having to help the kids. The minute that dressing-soaked lettuce hit his face, he muttered under his breath "De...nise!". Very much like Seinfeld says "Newman!" I smiled an evil smile when I heard the contempt in his voice. He didn't even wipe the dripping lettuce pieces from his face.

He walked over to a chaise lounge and set one plate of lasagna down. Before I could realize what was happening, he turned around with a handful of lasagna and threw it at me with such force, it actually hurt my boob. Never in my life have I had boob pain from someone throwing lasagna at me! I was so pissed! How dare he! And, to make matters worse, this was a new Ralph Lauren white t-shirt! (Ok, granted I ordered it from Nordstrom Rack for $15.00, but STILL!) I don't get a lot of new clothes. WHAT AN ASS!

I stood there shaking. Staring down at the red and orange splotch on my new shirt, that I had ordered for our dinner date in the back yard. I closed my eyes. When I opened them, I was sucked into a rage like nothing before. My left arm picked up the basket of rolls while my eyes stayed locked on the mutant hell lord. Then, like a pitching machine at a batting cage that has malfunctioned, I started heaving those buns at him, one after another. Thankfully, the kids thought we'd eat 12 rolls. They had been microwaved way too long and were hard as rocks. The perfect weapons. I could tell they hurt the way John was trying to protect himself and yelping after every bun that made contact.

But then, the zombie redneck began to pick up the buns and toss them back at me. OUCH! My God, they were like huge bullets. One hit me on the side of the head then got stuck in my hair. Just a big hard sourdough bun hanging in my hair. Urgh! And I looked so nice tonight! I was distracted only for a moment, at how my new shirt was ruined, I had a bun dangling in my hair, and he's messed up how nice I looked tonight, when I felt a huge slap in my face from the other serving of lasagna. IN MY FACE! What kind of man does this! Fucking wad of dick!

I picked the slab off my face and immediately did the "retaliation hurl" right back at him. Sometimes my throwing ability is right on. Like major league pitching pro-amazing-ness. Other times, it's beyond sucking. (Like the time I was in 7th grade and our town had a fake Olympics for the whole community. I signed up for the softball toss. My friend Maria went before me, pretty great throw. Then, when I went, I totally spazzed, and the ball went like seven feet. This woman ACTUALLY came up to me and asked if I wasn't supposed to be in the "Special" Olympics. True story. Not that there's anything wrong with the Special Olympics. Simply an example of how sometimes, I cannot throw.)

My lasagna throw went low. REALLY low. It hit directly at the point where his foot stepped. He had started to take a few running steps towards the pool when I tossed it. When that foot came down on the lasagna, he slipped full force down to the ground. Ha! Maybe my throw was pretty decent after all. He hit his chin on the concrete with some force, taking down a side table that had red candles on it with him. He immediately jumped to his feet, feeling his chin for blood. He ALWAYS does that! What a baby! Put his fingers on his chin, look at hand for blood, can't believe that there's no blood, puts his fingers back to his chin, looks again for blood, no blood again? Can't be! Fingers to chin again. TOTAL BABY!

John: "You are such a fucking bitch."

Me: "Boo hoo, baby go boom? Did baby hurt his chinny winny?"

We both leaned down and grabbed a bun at the exact same time, and threw it...at the exact same time. Mine hit him in the crotch, his hit me in the nose. He immediately grabbed his crotch. I immediately grabbed my nose. We even said simultaneous "FUCK YOU!"s. That was pretty spectacular, I have to admit. Like stereo "fuck you's" in the back yard that echoed off our back wall. Bitchen. (You know, it's really sad to me that the kids today don't say "bitchen". That was such a cool word! "Have a bitchen summer!" How many times did I write that in people's yearbooks??? SO MANY! "Stay bitchen!" So freaking cool. What is it now? All "my bitches" and "brah's". I don't know, bitchen was a word that sounded like a bad word, so you got to feel cool saying it, but at the same time, it had a positive meaning. Yea, my pink ditto jeans in 8th grade were...bitchen!)

Anyway, after the dual "bun fuck you's", Andrew ran out and found us furious at each other, John holding his crotch, me holding my nose. He grabbed

John and just started pulling him to the love seat. I kept yelling at him as Andrew drug him away.

Me: "Go sit your baby ass on your little flowery ass love seat you pussy ass excuse of a man!"

(Note to self: Do I use the word "ass" too much? Ponder that at some point and get back to me. Thanks.)

Andrew looked at me, with both fear and a, well, a kind of...disgust? It threw me for a minute. I actually paused before I yelled again, because...I actually don't think I've ever seen Andrew look at me like that before. It stung. Even in my over the top incensed state of rage, it hurt. But, it didn't stop me.

Me: "That is, if your ass fits you wide load lard butt fucker!"

It only took about four minutes and John came running out. He didn't say a word. He just picked me up, put me over his shoulder and immediately walked us back to the love seat. Yes I was freaking out. Was I hitting him? Nah. Not my style. I *was* however, reaching back with my left hand and pulling at whatever hairs I could get my fingers around, on top of his shiny balding head! I was...beyond furious! BEYOND! I screamed!

Me: "The second you put me on that thing I'm getting up! This continues! This is not OVER!"

He sat me down on the love seat and...instant...relief. A warm ocean of soft water flowing over my skin. It flowed gently over the negativity and covered it with a thick desire for peace and harmony. Such a beautiful feeling. Such a complete feeling. Joy. Beauty. A soul that understands the importance of love. How can this feeling be so, so, SO very different from the one I felt merely seconds ago? Truly this love seat holds a strong magic. Who ever thinks magical things don't exist in this world, are fools. I took a deep breath and opened my eyes.

John.

Me: "I'm sorry honey."

John chuckled, and leaned over and kissed me, on the lips, slow...and quite long. :)

I opened my eyes and smiled at him.

Me: "So...how'd we do?"

We both broke into a big laugh about my question.

John: "Actually honey, we didn't do that bad. We could have played things differently and it would have been fine, you understand that right?"

Me: "What...like me coming to sit on the love seat while you went to the kitchen to help the kids?"

John: "That, or, you could have come with me. We could have continued talking and laughing and we could have helped the kids together. I think we would have been fine. We were fine up until that point, that's the key. We did do it. We were able to, well, at least have the salad served and sit and talk for a while. We can do it Denise. I know we can."

His words gave me such confidence. Such strength. I knew he was right. I felt it. I knew it. I had total 100% faith in what he said. I knew we could do it too.

Me: "You think we can do it, do you?"

I actually said that rather suggestively, if I do say so myself. ;) ;) ;) (Oh yes I did just make THREE winky faces!)

John: "Absolutely. I know we can, you see, if we can…"

I interrupted him by taking his hand and pulling him off the sofa. I started leading him upstairs to our bedroom.

Me: "Not what I meant John."

I turned and winked at him. Muhahahah. I'm so bitchen! ;)

Denise, Next Morning

Well THAT was fun. :) Yea, I'm talking about last night. Ooooooh la la. I think that was pretty excellent actually. As sex goes. For being married this long. I don't think people expect to have sex like that after 14 years of marriage. I didn't expect to have sex like that, PLS. (Pre Love Seat.) I like to feel like I'm unique with the whole sex thing. But, I mean, I want to do different things. I don't know if I'm "Fifty Shades" material but something about that bothers me anyway. I mean, that book made bondage so mainstream. Now soccer moms, accountants and hipsters are using neck ties for bondage. Blech. I don't like mainstream. My brain rejects mainstream. I personally feel there's a new and unique and different type of sex to be had in the world. I know there is! Everyone is so boring. The whole romance thing is for the birds. Candles? Roses? Silky white nightgowns? BLECH! But I have the same reaction to the whole Fifty Shades thing. At least in that book. I'm sorry but I'm calling Christian Grey out! I think he's a poser. I mean, if he were all 'Mr. Sadist, this is all I know'...grrr. Is he really going to stop and change his whole being for one, not so cute, scrawny girl that never even wore a thong before? WTH? I don't know. I was all, "Oooh he's so mean and tough" and the next minute he freaking forgets the contract!??? What happened to Christian Grey!? NOOOOOO! So if Christian isn't actually hardcore and true to his roots...who is?

I don't know, there must be something else. What else is there? There's people who are into the whole baby thing. But I swear to god, they must be people who have never had a baby. Considering the amount of poop you commit to cleaning off a tiny behind when you have a baby...I absolutely CRINGE at the thought of a grown man pooping in his diapers. Cleaning poop off a grown man's hairy butt, is probably enough to push me over the edge to actually commit suicide.

Bestiality? Um. REALLY? Who are these sad, desperate people, that they can't find a human to do the dirty nookie deed with? I mean, WHAT? Does this really happen? No really. Does it? I can tell you, I'm not about to do a Google search for this and see what turns up. NO WAY. I would totally hire a gigolo before I'd do a hippo. Gigolo?

Wait. What are male whores called? Speaking of another thing that is unfair, a girl can just wear a low cut top, and suddenly she's a whore, slut, whatever. I see guys with NO shirts on watering their lawn. OMG why are the men watering their lawns shirtless NEVER attractive? Ever? ALWAYS guys with big guts and graying chest hair. So clearly they must be sluts. Right? Ugly ass slutty, shirtless, scary, gutty old guy lawn water-ers! I don't want to see that, no gracias. If a woman watered her lawn with no shirt on, that'd be a little slutty, yes?

So…are guys considered whores? Sluts? Are guys considered prostitutes? Because when I think of a prostitute I think of females. Are there guy hookers? Hmm. Hooker has a female connotation also. Are you seriously telling me all guys have is "gigolo"? And that stupid word sounds like an act at Cirque del Soleil. Doesn't sound bad at all. Slut, sounds bad. Whore…sounds *bad*. But, who can you ask questions like this to in life? So not Googling "male whore" either! I often fantasize about Googling something like that - "male whores", clicking on a few links that show me where to get a male whore, how much per hour, how much for blow job, etc. etc. Then…I die the next day. The family gathers around going through my personal things, and see that I was searching out "male whores" the day before I died. And, I'm not even there to explain. This is why I can't Google any crazy stuff. I have "Google-Death-Traumatic-Stress". Yes it's a condition. It's also not like I'm just going to just sit John down and say "Hey, so, do people really get it on with animals? Oh, and what's a male whore called?"

I peek over the top of my laptop at him. He probably wouldn't mind answering. But see, I don't want people to actually know that I think about all this stuff. I could ask in an online forum but...yea, I'm afraid of the answers. I don't need religious people breathing down my neck telling me I'm going to hell. I am just curious, are there really people sick enough in this world to do it with an animal? I mean, I'd rather rob a bank. Someone's house. Robbing I get. Money is the objective. That makes sense. But, getting down with a goat? Maybe only mentally unstable people do this. I mean, I can't picture attorneys and doctors going out to the farm for a weekend of fun. So bizarre.

John: "Whatcha writing over there honey? You look so serious."

Totally startled that he asked me what I was writing. Gah! Darn it. I feel my cheeks getting hot and red now too. Urgh. Busted. Sometimes I feel like John is actually able to see every crazy thought I have going on in my head. Urgh, he's not saying anything, just sitting there smiling at me. Grrrrr!

Me: "Just thinkin'."

I smile and try to make myself seem normal. Difficult task.

John: "Hmmmm. If I didn't know better, I'd think you were having one of your crazy daydreams again."

Yay! A technicality!

Me: "Ha! Not at all. Nice try. I was just thinking about...all this."

Don't judge. That was a truthful answer. I was indeed thinking about "all this"…as in, weird sex acts. And it wasn't a "daydream", it was musings. Ponderings. :) Just shush.

He chuckled and looked back down to his computer. Right. We have to figure out this whole "going to Molly's play thing". Stay focused. Stay on track. This is important. Our life! I look back down to my computer and see the word "bestiality". Hmmm. I suddenly visualize my orthopedic doctor doing it with a zebra. Oh god…YUCK!

So, what kind of new sex is there out there? We have the whole dominant, submissive thing. GRRRR, what I really hate is when people switch that up. I like people to be true to what they are. If you're dominant, be dominant. I can't take you seriously if you handcuff me one day and you're all angry and controlling in my face and the next day you're licking my shoe. (ICK… I live in Los Angeles. That shoe will no doubt have feces, dog urine, and old gum on it.)

If you are baby man one day, you can't be my parent the next day. If you're doing a goat, you can't want a human the next. Huh? What am I saying. Well, my point is, there has to be something new…and exciting. Food sex? Hmm. Ehhh. Sushi? Meatloaf? Macaroni and cheese? Grapefruit? Mmmm...no!

Public sex? That's not so public, of course. I guess there's the whole "mile high club" thing. And with that, you just have to follow with, how could that possibly be comfortable. You'd have dents in your legs from all those buttons in there. I try to picture sex in an airplane bathroom. I can't see how you could actually have sex without accidentally hitting the "call button". Do the "plane workers", "stewards", um, "air attendants"? (What the heck is the politically correct word for male "stewardesses"? Because there are certainly as many men as women now. Hmm. Should look that up one day. Add it to the list of things to Google.)

So do those people who work in planes, have some sort of override to be able to get into the bathrooms on planes? OMG another thing to Google! What did people do before Google! They were dumb. Google makes everyone smart.

Oh. My. God. DENISE! FOCUS! Yes I am yelling at myself inside my head! Geez, if anyone ever knew how I think, I wonder if I'd be committed? I wonder if other people think the way I do. Thoughts just rambling through your brain all day. Daydreams as vivid as any movie. STOP!!!! DENISE!!!!!!

Ok. I'm stopped.

Tonight is the play. We must succeed at this. In just a few hours, we could come back to this house, play behind us, and know…that we have a life off of this love seat. Suddenly a wave of excitement rolled through my body. A normal life! Yes! Ok. Down to business.

Denise, Evening of Play

We are ready to go. I have my iPad. I have all my jokes, videos, photos and funny memories all ready to go at a push of the button. I feel really bad for the people back in the 18th century who had this same issue. Poor people stuck on love seats with no iPad. Must have been horrible. John has everything on his phone. Andrew has a joke book and several stunt falls ready. See, I don't know why, but it really tickles me when people fall down. I once paid Jamie Woodward in second grade fifty cents to fall over in his desk. The old school desks with the arm attached that had the writing/desk part on it. They were big and heavy and made a huge crashing sound. He really had to get that baby rocking to get it to tip over. Only problem was I honestly almost peed when he did it, I laughed so hard. I also paid Jamie fifty cents to hide in the coat closet after lunch. Which he did. When class started again, there was no way he could just exit the closet in the middle of class. Jamie stayed in that closet until the bell rang to end school at 2:50 pm. Kids just went to get their coats, Jamie exited, no one really cared. But I still laugh about that! That kid was crazy.

Amber, the intellectual girl that she is, has quotes from literature that she finds amusing?

Uhhhh….okayyyyyy. I can't see that reciting some clever quip from Shakespeare during one of our "anger freak out sessions" is going to do any good at all. Gotta love Amber. :) Maybe she could recite lines from *Twilight*, now that's comedy!

John has a huge collection of things. He's been working so hard on whatever he put on his phone. He won't even tell me everything, as he wants it to be a surprise, to catch me off guard with his satchel of funny goods. All I know about are the photos of my mom. Lol. Just knowing that John has photos of my mom with sayings on his phone, makes me laugh. He's going to have to be extremely cautious though, because my parents are coming. Eeeeek! God I hope this goes well.

John: "Sweets, your parents are here."

As always, John startles me out of my thought-induced stupor. I jump up and get the door.

Me: "Hello Mama, Hello Dada."

Dad raises his eyebrows to see me off the love seat. I smile at him.

Mom: "You're...not...?"

She looks to the love seat. She looks to John standing, getting his technology together.

I haven't bothered explaining to my mom about what's going on. She's religious. She's not into the mystical, supernatural, etc. She'd never understand this. It's beyond the scope of what her brain can recognize as earthly possibilities. She would consider it black magic, the devil's work, Satan...

Mom: "You can be off the love seat without getting mad at each other? No fighting?"

My jaw drops and I look at John. He shrugs. Nah, he wouldn't have explained all that to my mom. I look at my dad. Dad is smiling at me, looking like he was a six year old who just got in trouble.

Me: "Oh, so Dad told you. Well…"

I look back to my mom, she just has the weirdest look on her face. I have to laugh. But…then again, when you're the only one in a room laughing, said laughter becomes a very short- lived event. : (

Me: "Yes Mom, sorry, you see, we have found that we are okay for a bit before we have to get back on the love seat. John can stay off longer than I can with no ill effects. However…if we are laughing and the mood is very light, we can stay off a lot longer. We had a trial run last night, we had dinner out there."

I look outside, ehhhh, maybe we should have cleaned up. My mom turns her head to look outside and sees the horrible mess.

Mom: "Right. So that went well then?"

Grrrrr! My mom is so snarky.

Me: "Well, we had some minor issues but we understand how to fix them now."

I smile a totally fake, gooey smile at her. My "YMCA smile" as John calls it. I once had to take a photo for my YMCA membership card. I'm not a big fan of people taking stupid photos of me. I guess my smile was pretty revealing as in "I'm really not into you taking my photo and I really wish you'd hurry your ass up!" I had to live with that stupid photo on the membership card for so long. Every time I had to show it to get into the workout room, EVERY single time, the kid who swiped the card would do a double take at my horribly fake smile. Thus, "YMCA smile."

My dad is smiling, but I know my dad. He looks scared shitless. I can't quite read my mom. Either she is really rooting for us, or...she is praying for the crash and burn, just like Goose. Either way, we are going to do this. This is our shot. Our chance at having a normal life. I look at John who moves to me and puts his arms around me. I close my eyes for a brief second to concentrate on my feelings for him. So strong. We are...a couple. We belong together. I smile at him. It's one of the wonders of the world. Out of all these billions of people on this planet. To actually find the one you're supposed to be with. Incredible.

Molly comes downstairs in her Annie costume. Oh, she looks so, SO adorable. My little girl is SUCH the actress! Tonight is her very special night and I am beyond thrilled that John and I get to experience this not only together, but in love. :)

Me: "Molly! You look incredible! So cute!"

John: "Awww, Molly! You are the perfect Annie!"

Andrew: "Molly you look great!"

Amber: "Your shoes are leather. You know these days they make shoes that look like leather that aren't really leather."

Everyone shoots Amber a quick look.

Dad: "You are the best Annie EVER!"

Mom: "Isn't the wig a little...off?"

I roll my eyes at Mom. She's always so..."Mom". She's not about to ruin this night. No way.

Me: "Nope, the wig is perfectly perfect, wonderful, couldn't be more perfect. Looks like the real thing. Looks better than any Annie I've EVER seen!"

John rolled one eye at me, expressing his displeasure for me having gone into over the top defensive mode about Molly's wig. How the hell did he do that? Roll one eye? WTH? I never knew he could do that. Damn, that comes in handy when you don't want people to see you rolling your eyes at them! Simply turn your head so they can't see your rolling eye, and roll away. I really need to learn that trick. John looks back to the room.

John: "Well everyone, it's going to be an exciting evening. We all have our roles. Barb, Steve, we're going to need you to help also."

John hands them a couple of pages each, stapled together.

John: "We have found, that when Denise and I are off of the love seat, as long as things are light hearted, funny, happy…we are OK. We are moving forward based on that, and that is why we are having this night out. As a family. These are some jokes. Hopefully if things go bad, you two can also help lighten the mood. We'd really appreciate your help."

John stops, waiting for their response. Of course my dad speaks up .

Dad: "Absolutely John. We will help in any way possible."

My mom is looking down at the jokes on the papers before her, frowning.

Mom: "What do you call a mushroom that goes into a bar and buys drinks for everyone all night long?"

OMG! I swear to you! I don't think I've EVER heard my mom tell a joke! Suddenly every single one of us bursts out laughing! Well, everyone except Mom. Then Mom keeps reading...

Mom: "A fungi to be around?"

Except she says "fun-ghee" not "fun guy", which, for some reason makes it even more hysterical that she doesn't even get the joke. The kids are laughing so hard. LOL! I think we will be fine tonight. As long as my mom has enough material. John is still laughing when he speaks.

John: "Ok, Barb, that's terrific. Well done. You will be a big help. We really appreciate this."

My dad is laughing as he puts his arm around Mom. She is still frowning, looking through the pages of her assigned jokes. She's not a "joke" person. Something about a really conservative, heavy, not light person reading jokes in a very monotone way...pretty darn funny.

John: "Ok everyone, head out to the minivan, Denise and I will be there in a couple of minutes."

Everyone leaves out the front door and John and I sit on the love seat.

John: "I thought it would be good for us to get in a little 'sit' before we head off."

Me: "Yes, like fill up, before the road trip!"

John chuckles.

John: "Exactly. I figure, driving to the school, five minutes, the play starts at 7:30 and should be done by 9:00 pm, and five minutes home. So, my lady, do you think you have and hour and forty minutes to spare me…off of this love seat?"

Me: "Why, yes my Lord, I believe I do. John! I really want this to work. I want us to be free!"

John: "It will work Denise. Just believe it. And stay positive, at all costs. Our future totally depends on this. This is the rest of our lives we are talking about here. You know how bad things were, before this…"

He looks down to the love seat and glides a hand over it.

John: "For some reason Denise, this crazy little love seat, saved us. Saved US. You and me. Our marriage. We were always meant to be together. It was always you and I. Fate knew it. But we, we lost ourselves along the way. This piece of furniture showed us what was important. This love seat stripped away all the hatred and anger, and showed us the raw love we have for each other. I have no idea if this is magic. If this is a gift from God. Witchcraft? I honest to god have no clue how or why this love seat has done this for us. But here's what I know. I never want to lose this Denise. I never want to lose you. You are…the love of my life. "

I lean over and kiss him. :)

Me: "We're going to do it John. I know we are. "

We give each other one last hug before getting up and heading to the door. As I walk out, I turn and give the love seat a big smile and blow a kiss to it.

The car ride to the school is great. Granted it is only five minutes, but we are laughing the whole way. It feels so good, to be free. In the car. Driving along. Windows open, fresh air coming in. My hair blowing. Dad and John talking in the front seat, like always. My mom and I in the middle with Molly between us. Amber and Andrew in the back fighting. SO GREAT! Every little thing I used to take for granted is so crystal clear at this moment. How amazing life is. How real it all is. To be around the people that love you in this life. My mom is fiddling with Molly's hem. Plucking at the tiniest little thread. Normally that would have bothered me so much, but I just smile and say, "That looks better Mom." Mom raises an eyebrow at me. Lol. I don't care. I'm elated. Filled with tremendous joy. I can't imagine having even one negative feeling. This is going to be the greatest night of my life.

:)

We hustle Molly backstage to the volunteer parents who are overseeing everything. The drama teacher is in a bit of a frenzy. He calls to Molly when he sees her.

Teacher: "Yes! Miss Hannigan, over here please!"

Molly looks over her shoulder completely confused and points at herself fully dressed in her "Annie" attire. Lol. Pretty awesome, a seven year old doing a total slapstick "Who, me?" I tell Molly that I am sure he is just stressed out, it's a big night for a first grade drama teacher, and push her over to him and the other kids he is talking to.

I really don't get all the "volunteer parents". The ones who always sign up for "class mom" first. Who fight and push each other aside to be the "field trip volunteers." I don't know. Do you think they're just a little "too" involved in their kids lives? Those are also the moms who sit there during their kids' entire practices, watching every little thing their kid does and yelling in the car at them on the way home. Urgh. Yucko.

I assess my state of mind as I walk back around to the auditorium where our seats are. We are there pretty close to showtime, as we don't want to spend any unnecessary time away from home. ;) I feel good. I'm pretty concerned about Molly. I haven't even thought about John and I. Interesting. I still feel happy. Confident. It is getting my drivers license all over again. It is freedom. Independence. The ability to walk around in the world. Do things. Be a part of things. I can't believe how much you take for granted on a daily basis. To simply be able to walk my seven year old back stage for her play, I cherish it. I walk up the aisle to the seats near the back. "Near the back" is fine with me. In case we need to make a hurried exit or I need to start throwing the tic-tacs in my purse at John's head. One never knows. I laugh to myself. When I get to our seats John smiles at me. I think he is in a bit of disbelief that I've walked up smiling. He hugs me and kisses me.

John: "You're sitting right here pretty girl."

He moves out to the aisle so I can get in. Andrew is on my right. Then Mom, Amber, and Dad taking up the side. Seemed like a good arrangement. The men on the edges, like "row bouncers" in case anything gets out of hand. But I swear, I feel so great. I just can't picture anything going wrong. John leans in to whisper.

John: "Honey, how do you feel?"

Me: "I feel great! Like I can't believe it. It's easy. I had no problems dropping Molly. I'm totally happy! "

I squeeze around his waist with my left arm. He takes my face in both his hands and kisses me. We part and smile at each other. Then I turn to my right to check on everyone just in time to see my mom roll her eyes. Lol. Oh Mom. Suddenly I feel breath again in my left ear.

John: "Denise…"

I turn back to him.

Me: "Yes?"

John: "Do you remember…"

Me: "YES??"

This seems like it is going somewhere kinky.

John: "When I jumped out of bed to close the sliding door and save the dogs from the coyotes, but my feet got stuck on the sheets and I fell to the floor?"

Damn! I wasn't expecting that! I totally burst out laughing. To which my mom gives another eye roll. Omg, that was so funny. We live in an area of Los Angeles that has quite a bit of wild life. Dogs have gotten eaten by coyotes in our area. So, any time we hear coyotes outside, we close our doors so the dogs can't go outside. Yes, it makes for more urine piles around our home, but hey, at least our dogs are alive. I was totally asleep. I woke up to John, on the floor, struggling in the sheets tied around his ankles. Physical comedy...is so funny to me! I can't help it. Especially unplanned physical comedy. He couldn't have planned that any better if he tried. What in the world was happening in his sleep that caused him to be completely bound at the ankles in the sheets? I was laughing so hard and so was John. He gets really tickled when he's able to get me into my uncontrollable laughter stage.

Urgh, April Miller turns around to give me the evil eye. Class mom type. She hates me. I hate her too. Blech. I don't understand how a mom has the time to make that many play dates for her kid. She has to make sure her child is most popular. Makes play dates for her daughter with the most popular kids. Gets the teachers amazing gifts. Takes them out to lunch. Facebooks and instagrams the teachers. At the annual silent auction, she bids $2,000.00 on "lunch with your teacher" so no one else can bid on it. And, get this, last year at the end of the school year, she has a big bash, a welcome summer end of the school year huge party, and doesn't invite six girls? Huh? Who does that? Who purposely invites all the first graders, except for six girls? What sort of evil sloth Gucci wearing bitch does that? April Miller that's who! I glare back at her until she gives up and turns her bleached little head around. Urgh.

I turn to John who is just watching me give April the stare down.

John: "Everything good in there?"

He knocks on my head. Lol. He cracks me up sometimes.

Me: "Blech…just that disgusting woman down there. She bugs the crap out of me!"

John: "Honey, I know she does. And we can plot our class mom take over soon and really burn her ass. But for now, our first night out off the love seat, can we concentrate on being happy? My love?"

I can't help it. I laugh.

Me: "OMG John, can we really? Next year, can we camp out overnight, be first in line, and sign up for class mom? Beat her at her own game! That'll send her over the edge not to have that control! John can we please????"

John starts laughing but also looking around a little paranoid and gives me a tiny, baby "Shhhh" sign with this finger on his lips.

John: "Denise, you realize we are surrounded by class moms? We are in enemy territory. You can't just speak out like that! They will make us…for the rebellious non-PTA types that we are!"

I laugh. God, I love this guy! My love thoughts are interrupted by the announcer. Franco, Molly's seat partner. Awww. He looks so cute in his tiny tux.

Franco: "Good evening ladies and gentlemen. Welcome to Paradise Valley's first grade production of *Annie*. There will be a short intermission in 35 minutes. Please refan from going to the bathroom until that time. And please turn your cell phone's volume off. Thank you, and OH, reFRAIN. Sorry. OK bye."

Awww, he is a little flustered that he misspoke. Cute. I squeeze John's hand. The play is starting. The curtains open and there are the girls in the orphanage. All the beds set up. And there is my Molly. Looking ever adorable. :)

We last until the intermission just fine. I'm so enthralled with Molly. How amazing she is. How incredible her singing is. Honestly, I never thought once about our problem. About being off the love seat. About even slightly hating John. It all feels so natural. So easy. We go out to the lobby for punch and packaged cookies. I hate packaged cookies. They just taste like sweet cardboard. And they all have hydrogenated oil in them. But, far be it from me to pass up a cookie. Even a cardboard one. We are just about at the end of the intermission, when April appears in my face. GRRRRR.

April: "Oh, hi Denise honey, how arrrrreeeeeee you. You look…(OMFG she actually pauses and looks me up and down before she finishes that thought! BITCH!)…great."

Wow, that is the most insincere "great" I have EVER heard in my life.

April: "Oopsie!"

She reaches over and picks a dog hair off my shirt! WTF!!!!!!!!!!!!!!!!!!!! Suddenly I am in a tornado of rage. Spinning. The fog rolls in. My world shifts. Suddenly we are on the Orca, out at sea. Attempts to kill the shark have failed. I am Brody. Richard Dreyfuss is Hooper, but he doesn't look like Hooper from the movie. He is his character from the Goodbye Girl, playing Richard III, in a purple smock, holding a nosegay, with a humpback...on the boat! What the hell is going on in my mind? Our boat has been compromised. The shark is on the deck...it's mouth open... and April's leg is in it's mouth. It's weird because the shark totally doesn't look real. It's obvious it's the mechanical one from Universal Studios, but April is screaming in pain.

Richard: "Now is the winter of our discontent..."

April: "ARRRGGGG HELP ME!!!!!!!"

I am thrilled. I am so happy to see her bloody leg in that Universal Studios shark's mouth. I'm grinning from ear to ear. Looking from April back to Richard. He is trying to limp around the tilted boat, slipping on the water as he goes. He squats a bit and looks right at the shark.

Richard: "Are YOU the son of York?"

One of the shark's mechanical eyes closes. There is a tiny bit of smoke coming from the malfunctioning eye. The other eye remains open. So now the shark is "winking." April is screeching louder as the shark takes her in his mouth, from the waist down. I can't help it, I just start laughing.

Richard: "A horse, a horse, my kingdom for a horse!"

Me: "A horse?"

Oops. I realize that I've said that out loud. I snap out of my daydream quickly to see April frowning at me.

April: "A horse? What?"

She looks down at the hair between her fingers.

April: "Looks like a dog hair to me honey."

She laughs. Ohhhh! That is it. I can't handle it. I have these feelings of anger in me, like the ones that I have felt towards John. But they are directed at April. God damnit her hair is perfect! Whose hair looks like that? WTH? It is like pageant hair. It looks fake. Too blonde. Too much hair spray. Too much shimmer. Just too much!

Me: "What the fuck is up with your hair?"

I guess I say that a little loud, because literally, the entire room stops. Attorney dads, soccer moms, doctor moms, engineer dads...kids, teens, babies, tweens...they all turn around to look at me. But the look on April's face, lol! She is stuck in a thin area of confusion. She knows by the tone of my voice that I have insulted her hair, but since I didn't actually say an insult, she doesn't know what to do. Half her face is confused, half is angry.

April: "Excuse me?"

Everyone within fifteen feet of me is waiting for my response.

Me: "Your hair April, it looks like an ugly ass wig on a mannequin displaying pageant dresses. Honey boo boo much?"

Most of the tweens around me start laughing, including Amber. But my response is all it takes for the family to jump into "comedy mode". Andrew immediately runs towards April, slightly bumps her and then goes rolling about ten feet away on the ground. That would have been enough to snap me out of it, it's hilarious to see him rolling through the crowd with people parting to let him roll through, but EVERYONE goes into full arrest comedy routines.

John puts his phone in front of my face, playing a clip from our wedding video where we were talking about how lame our friend's wedding was. Omg! She can never see that! Amber is reading from her papers.

Amber: "Mom! There live not three good men unchanged in England; and one of them is fat." She starts laughing but none of the rest of us do. Amber's sense of humor can be...unique.

Dad is so nervous. The papers in his hands are shaking and his voice cracks as he speaks.

Dad: "Denise! What do you call a short psychic who escaped from jail? A SMALL MEDIUM AT LARGE!"

He even does the obligatory fake laugh after his joke to try and infect me, get me to laugh. I look at my mom, who is clearly shuffling through her pages to find a joke she even slightly understands. That is all it takes.

I start laughing so hard. But she never pays attention to anyone but herself. She doesn't even notice that the crisis has been averted. April just walks away, thinking we are, perhaps, the largest group of weirdos that has ever attended a function at Paradise Valley elementary school. What that must look like, for me to get slightly pissed, then to have my entire family jump into comedy mode? Lol! Hilarious. OMG…my mom finally decides on a joke. She clears her throat and goes for it.

Mom: "Having sex is like playing bridge. If you don't have a good partner, you'd better have a good hand."

She totally second guesses herself after she says the joke. But it is too late. Everyone who hears that bursts into uncontrollable laughter. John has to hold himself up with the refreshment table. Mom continues squinting at her paper, trying to decide exactly what that meant.

Mom: "Wait a minute…"

Suddenly she has a very shocked look on her face and turns bright red.

Mom: "I thought this was a bridge joke…"

She trails off as her face became more red. Dad is crying with laughter. The lights flicker on and off and everyone starts moving back to their seats. Mom is led back to her seat by my dad guiding her elbow. She just continues to silently mouth that joke over and over again. Horrified that she told a dirty joke. I whisper to John.

Me: "John, did you do that on purpose? Give Mom a dirty joke?"

John just winks at me and starts laughing. We are all still laughing when we get to our seats. My laughter stops short when April turns around to snarl at me. I growl back, then let out a small bark. Ha! She turns right around. I don't care if she thinks I'm crazy!

John suddenly looks on edge because I had stopped laughing and barked. I know what he is thinking.

Me: "Honey, it's OK. I'm fine. I just hate that woman, but I'm happy and fine, see?"

I lean over and kiss him on the cheek.

Me: "You're my guy, you always will be, and I loaf you like a warm crusty sourdough round loves clam chowder."

He laughs and hugs me as the lights go down again. We've made it. We drove to the school, went through the first part of the play...got through intermission with April the pageant-haired soccer mom, with NO problems. I know the family thought I was losing it there with April, but I wasn't. I never hated John. I could care less if I rage at April. What matters is that John and I have been absolutely fine for FIFTY MINUTES! YES! Only fifty minutes to go. We can do that.

Molly is a little dream. Hits every line, never forgets a word. She is a bit taller than Daddy Warbucks, played by her classmate Brandon. That's kind of amusing. Especially when they dance together. Molly looks like she is going to swing little Brandon off the stage. Lol. John and I hold hands, laugh and cheer so loud for Molly. It's been a very long time since we've been out enjoying ourselves like this. Absolutely wonderful.

My mom finally relaxes after her "hand job" joke and is laughing with my dad at the small first graders making such an amazing effort to pull off *Annie*. Andrew and Amber seem to be having a terrific time also. Although I did notice Andrew glancing at John and I every couple of minutes, so afraid something would go wrong I'm sure. What is odd is, I *know* nothing will go wrong. I feel completely in control. I have zero negative feelings towards John. I just know it isn't going to happen. No way. This feels too good. The happiness is overwhelming. No one can mess with it or take it away. Every minute we last, only makes me more excited and thrilled. I can tell John feels the same way. I don't think we'll be able to sleep tonight. I picture us talking all night about our incredible success. Talking about what this means for us. For our future! All the things we want to do together. :) We have missed out on so much over these past years. The "dark years" we'll call them. Now we have reached the light. I'm going to be like my grandparents. I'll be the old lady, shopping in the big underwear section at J.C. Penny's, John will be the old man with a cane, yelling at me to just grab any pair and hurry up. Lol. My grandaddy used to get so annoyed with my grandmom taking too long, anywhere! Market, store, bank. Everyday he got more impatient. He'd literally be in a store 5 minutes before he'd be ready to go. He would come visit, say he was staying the weekend until Sunday, and he'd end up leaving Saturday at 5 a.m. Lol Can't wait!

The play ends and the room erupts with huge waves of cheers and applause. If I may say so myself, Molly gets the biggest round of applause. Maybe that's because I am screaming my head off and can't hear anyone else. One never knows.

I run around and collect Molly as John brings the car around. We all pile in ready for the last 5 minutes in the car. FIVE MINUTES more and we have made it! A NIGHT OUT!

Me: "Guys, you realize that nothing went wrong? Nothing! We did it! "

Andrew: "Um, except that you almost attacked Mrs. Miller."

Me: "Andrew, I did not almost attack her! I verbally attacked her hair, but I was in total control! I was fine! And I certainly didn't hate your father. By the way, nice stunt fall there."

Everyone laughs...but...when I say those words "hate your father..." something in me stirs. I feel a twinge. My eye twitches. I feel a coldness in my finger tips. But I know I can handle it. We will be home in three minutes and I can get on the love seat. As everyone continues to talk about the night, I concentrate on what this means for me. For us. That I can go to the market. We can go out to dinner. As a family, or just John and I on a date. I suspect that we will be able to stay out longer and longer as we get used to it. An hour and 40 minutes is pretty amazing for our first time out together. I just keep feeding myself positive ideas. Telling myself what I am going to do first. Where I am going to go. I actually really need to stock up on my bathroom supplies. Deodorant. Toothpaste. Shampoo. I plan the trip to the drugstore in my head. Make my list. Just keep adding to it. Sunscreen. Lip gloss. Body wash. Mascara. Q-tips. Detangler. Face soap. Tweezers. I look up to see we are just a couple of streets from home. OK, I can do this. A new loofa. Razor replacements. New toothbrushes. Whitening strips for John. Emergency packs. Saline solution. Body lotion. Hair clips. I look up again! Yes! We are home.

I can tell John knows something is up because he looks at me questioningly in the rear view mirror. But I don't want to risk talking to him. Saying anything that would ruin our amazing evening. So I throw open my car door and race to the front door. Oh crap. John has the keys.

Me: "JOHN! OPEN!"

That is all I can get out. I just start banging on the front door. Andrew screams.

Andrew: "DAD! Open the door! Hurry!" Poor kid. He's really worried things will revert to the way they used to be. That must have sucked so bad for the kids. John trips out of the car he is trying to hurry so hard. He doesn't fall but takes several steps to catch himself. Which, for some reason, really pisses me off!

Me: "What the hell! Why are you such an uncoordinated spaz?!"

John's expression drops. He looks pale as a ghost. I don't think he was expecting me to lose it quite so quickly. He sprints to the front door. But he is so nervous now, that his hands are shaking and he can't open the door. Everyone is screaming at him.

Dad: "Come on son, hurry up there!"

Amber: "DAD! OPEN THE DOOR!"

Andrew: "Oh my god, come ON Dad!"

Molly: "Daddy! Can't you hurry?"

Mom: "Oh John, you simply put the key into the little opening and turn. Simple really."

I laugh at what my mom says.

Me: "Yeah John, any moron can figure it out!"

Mom and I share a glance. I know it doesn't make her "happy" when John and I hate each other. But, it does make her *happy*. I look at John struggling with the key. What an idiot. He looks so feeble. So scared. Such a puny man. I know it will freak him out, so I grab the keys and chuck them as hard as I can towards the street. Lol! The look on his face! Utter shock. Only Mom and I are left at the front door. Everyone else takes off in a sprint towards the keys. Bunch of goons. So dependent on a stupid love seat. So desperate to get me on it. Meh. No one is going to make me sit on that stupid thing. I start walking briskly down the street.

John is the first to get to the keys, but when he sees me walking down the street, he switches gears and runs towards me.

John: "Steve, get the keys, open the front door!"

Oh no you don't! I start running. John starts running. Urgh. I really should work out more. I'm out of breath in like 20 yards. He catches up and grabs me. I don't know why, but I just freak out with him touching me and start yelling "Help, rape!" I'm so pissed his hands are on me! I guess he doesn't like me yelling "rape" much as he keeps putting his hand over my mouth. But I still get a few yells out as I'm wiggling and lashing about like a full grown dolphin in John's arms, out of the water.

Dad has gotten the keys and opened the front door. Mom just stands at the front door, not entering, looking at John and I. I notice her ever so slightly shaking her head at us. Like she is completely disgusted by us. Urgh!

Me: "WhatEVER Mom!"

Mom looks surprised that I've called her out on her snarky slight head shake.

Me: "Yea that's right! Just shut it! And as for you..."

I twist my head around to look at John.

Me: "You're an evil, fat, ugly..."

At which point he shoves me in the front door. At which point...At...which...point...the world...it is whooshing past me. Over and over. So fast. I can see the lines, the trails of the world, as everything rushes past me. Molly screams. I feel pin pricks all over my skin. Electric shock. A lump in my throat. A cold sweat. A ball of nausea in my stomach. Sadness. Hatred. Sickness. The...love seat...is...gone.

Our whole living room is a mess. The computers and TV's are gone. Lamps. I notice the drawer where I keep the silverware from our wedding, open and empty. We weren't just robbed, they took anything of value. But, the love seat? Why? No other furniture has been taken. Everyone stands there in shock for a good ten minutes before anyone says a word. Molly and Amber are crying. Andrew just slumps to the ground in a squat position, holding his head. I look at John. He is white. Pure white. He looks like he is dead. Embalmed. I look at my mom. She looks somewhat smug. Not smiling, just…content. Then I look at my dad, he has tears in his eyes. Dad speaks first.

Dad: "You need to call the police John."

Everyone stands there another five minutes before anyone else speaks. Of all the things taken, every single one of us just stares at the spot where the love seat had been. I am overwhelmed. So many feelings. I don't want to talk to any of them. I don't want to think about anything. I just want to go to bed. I walk upstairs, take off my shoes, and lay down on the bed. My eyes feel glassy and sad. My heart feels dark. My body barely has the energy to raise my arm and turn off the light. It feels like it takes ten minutes, to simply turn off the bedside lamp. I close my eyes and immediately sleep.

John

When tragedy strikes in your life, you always seem to ask yourself, "Why me?" I keep asking "Why me?" "Why tonight?" "Why us?" "Why the love seat?" So many questions. And yet no one to answer them. No one to give me comfort. I have never felt more alone.

I was actually relieved when Denise just walked upstairs and went to bed. I didn't want her to speak. I didn't want to deal with her emotions. I have so many of my own. Selfish? Maybe. But I couldn't. I just couldn't deal with anyone. I told Denise's parents to just go, that we'd figure out everything the tomorrow. The kids went to bed without a word.

The house is a mess. Stuff everywhere. But I can't be bothered. I feel so cold. So, oddly emotionless. Just still and cold. I came into the guest room, laid down on the bed and closed my eyes. I just want to be in a void space. I want to be nowhere. With no feelings. I concentrate very hard on being absolutely nowhere. Then I fall asleep.

I wake up in the exact position I fell asleep in. Haven't moved all night. I am so stiff, and still very cold. I sit up and just stare around the room. I don't think about anything for about an hour. Then I start thinking little by little about Denise. How I felt. Last night was an amazing night. For Denise and I, and for our family. I still feel some of that in me. I am trying to feel the happiness from last night, but it is more like I am remembering it, rather than it being me who actually experienced it. It is such a detached feeling. I just lay here trying to connect the feeling with myself. It was only last night. How can the love seat connect it so easily, within seconds for us? What is it about the love seat? Did it know us? Did the love seat contain our history? Our entire relationship? So that when we sat on it, every feeling, emotion, happy thought, good time, came rushing back? Was the love seat, like…one big memory? Or was it simply magic? I will never know now. I can't believe it's gone. That love seat was the greatest gift anyone could ever give someone. That love seat gave us our lives back. We were cold, bitter, useless humans before the love seat. We put our kids through hell, with our fighting back and forth. We can't do that again. I won't do that again. Denise and I need to do what we are going to do, and spare the kids what we put them through before. I decide to go talk to her.

When I get up to the bedroom, she is still asleep in her clothes from the play last night. She…she looks pretty. I know I can't be with her, but she looks pretty. And peaceful. I gently shake her shoulder.

Me: "Hey, Denise, wake up."

She opens one eye and immediately makes that sound in the back of her throat like she is utterly disgusted with me. I don't know why, but it makes me chuckle.

Me: "Yeah, yeah, I know. I'm the last thing you want to see when you're waking up. But please just listen to me, OK?"

She rolls her eyes and sits up. She bends her knees and hugs them with her arms. One piece of her hair is totally out of place on top. It's like it doesn't fit in with the rest of her head. A total rogue piece of hair. It seems to come out of the left hand side of her head...go out to the side, then turns ninety degrees straight up. It goes up for about two inches, then arcs over the top of her head. Spectacular really. Denise realizes my eyes aren't looking at hers, and she smoothes the top of her head with her hand. But, that doesn't fix the rogue strand. It is damn strong and not going anywhere. I look at her for about two minutes before I start talking.

Me: "Ok Denise. We gave it a try. We almost conquered it too. I know there is love between us, but there is also a lot of hatred and resentment built up over the years. Last night at the play, I know that I loved you more than anyone. I wanted to spend eternity with you. But today I wake up, and I can't get in touch with that feeling. I know it was there, but I can't *feel* it. It's...just...gone. I don't know how far we could have gotten with the love seat. I don't know if little by little we could have fixed everything, and lived happily ever after. But the love seat is gone now, and we have to make a decision. I won't live in this house and argue with you. I won't rage and fight constantly with you in front of the kids. They've been through enough. If you want to rage at me, I can move out now.

244

Until all this is settled. But we can't do that to them again Denise."

She looks down at the sheets in front of her, and rests her chin on her knees. I sit down on the chair and just wait. I don't know when she will speak, but I am OK with waiting. I lean back and thoughts about everything we've been through flash through my head. God, living on that tiny love seat. It was great! Who would have thought that a life restricted to a five foot long piece of furniture could bring so much joy. That those ugly flowered cushions could allow you to feel the love that was always there. I'm looking up to the cottage cheese ceilings, seeing all kinds of shapes in it. A car. Clouds. A dinosaur. Denise snaps me out of my thoughts.

Denise: "Yeah, you're right. I won't fight with you in front of the kids. Let's just avoid each other, in the house, until we can settle everything. We can sell the house and go our separate ways. Until then, you stay away from me. I'll stay away from you. Get anything you'll need from the bedroom, and then just leave me alone."

She looks, the tiniest bit...sad? I'm not sure if sadness is the emotion. But it seems like sadness. God, if the people who robbed us only knew what they had stolen. They stole the rest of our lives together. More valuable than any material thing. If they only knew.

I gather my things and take everything downstairs. Denise just stays in that position on the bed. Not looking at me. Just staring down at the sheets, until I finally leave the room.

Denise

I guess numb is the word to describe how I feel. I don't care. I don't care if John and I get divorced. I don't care if I never kiss him again. I don't care if we never have a night like last night again. I don't know why not being on that stupid love seat causes us to not love each other, but apparently it does. I could care less about him right now. I wouldn't say I feel the rage and anger I used to before the love seat, but I simply don't care about him. Don't care for him. Don't care to waste my breath talking to him. Just…don't…care.

He's right about the kids though. We can't forget them and treat them like we did before. John and I can work out a schedule to avoid each other until we sell the house and both get our own places. I decided to write him an email to go over the logistics.

TO: JohnMan101@gmail.com
From: DeniseluvsScones5@gmail.com
Topic: Logistics

Hey. So, I think there should be some sort of division to the house. Obviously you'll sleep in the guest room. I'll sleep upstairs. I'll eat in the kitchen, you can eat in the dining room. The kids can be on a rotating schedule to eat with each of us. You can use the living room for your TV and general space. I'll use the family room. If we need to cross into each other's space, let's loudly announce that we are coming through.

I'll never need to come in your guest room. You clean it, do whatever you need. You never come in my bedroom. I do agree with you, that we shouldn't put the kids through any more drama. They don't deserve that. Don't start on me and I won't start on you.

I assume you'll be contacting the attorney today. Please let me know what the status is. When he can file, how long this will take. How long we have to live with this. I need a date, to be able to stand this. I need to know when this will end.

Thanks.
D

"When this will end." I keep looking at those words. Such a bizarre sensation to know I loved him so much last night. To know last night I wanted to be his girl, forever...into the next life. I wanted to be by his side. And today, I could care less about him. Wanting to know "when this will end." Life...is really strange.

Why were John and I put through this? Why did we get a glimpse of what true love was? Why were we teased like that? Shown how amazing it can be, then stripped of it? It doesn't make any sense. I really wish I could find that store again. I was so lost that day. I was in such a fog. My heart was dying. I tried to find Tian again. That magical, dear, mysterious Asian man. He held the answer, but I couldn't find him. I drove all through Chinatown. Every single street. The store wasn't there. I would remember that street. But I could never find it again. I closed my eyes and retraced my steps in my head, of where I went that day. I pictured a little GPS map in my head. I saw the red line from where I drove that day - it slowly went from Santa Monica, to Century City, Beverly Hills, West Hollywood...then the line starts to blur...it starts squiggling all over, making loop de loops. Soon my whole map is covered with red circles and lines.

Am I not supposed to find Tian? Was that shop even real? Did the love seat actually exist? I open my eyes. Of course the love seat existed. I shake the stupid idea off. It existed. John and I knew it did. We had love. Now we don't. It's that simple. Who ever stole that love seat, and stole our love from us, should pay. They don't even know what they've done to us. They could have taken every single thing in this house…why an ugly old love seat. : (

I close my eyes again. I am still sitting on the bed, but now Tian was sitting on the end of the bed. Very clear. I open my eyes quickly to see if he was really there. Nope. I close my eyes again, and there he is.

Tian: "Hello Denise."

Me: "Hello Tian."

He just smiles at me. His hands clasped together resting on his thighs. A mischievous little smile. I semi-shake my head, with a questioning look in my eyes. Doesn't move him in the least. He just sits there smiling at me. Grrr. I usually win "stare-offs", but this time I give in. I don't want him to disappear. I have so many questions for him. I slightly open one eye, he really isn't there on my bed. The second I close it, there he is. My brain is so weird. I know I'll be completely off my rocker by the time I'm 75.

Me: "Tian, I'm glad you're here. I have so many questions for you."

Tian just smiles.

Me: "Tian, did I buy that love seat? Or did you just send it here? Where is your store? Can I go back there? Can you give me the address? Tian…that love seat is magic, isn't it? Is there any way to get it back? Please, please, it's so important. Please?"

He continues to smile. But he blinks. This very slow, methodical blink. I am mesmerized. The blink seems to take a full sixty seconds. I watch every eyelash go down, then back up again.

Tian: "Love exists nowhere, except in your heart."

I frown. He has answered none of my questions. Can't he see I am desperate? That I truly need help? I'm sure he can. Yet he just gives me a flowery, philosophical line of meaningless BS.

Me: "That is *not* what I asked you!"

Andrew: "What did you ask me?"

I abruptly open my eyes to see Andrew standing there at my doorway. Tian gone. He look so sad. He looks like he's been crying. : (

Me: "Oh sorry Andrew, I uh…nothing. I didn't ask you for anything. I was just confused for a minute. I'm not really myself. I'm not really sure what I'm saying. Sorry honey."

Andrew: "It's fine Mom, I just wanted to know if you wanted me to bring you some coffee. Dad made some."

Me: "Urgh, right. If *Dad* made it, I don't want…"

I realize the horrible tone in my voice and see Andrew visibly cringe.

Me: "Yes, of course. I'd love some coffee. Thank you so much."

I motion with my hands for him to come to me. He sits down on the bed and I just hug him. Put my arms around him, and don't let go for at least five minutes. We just sit there. We both know the future. It sucks. He was as fooled as we were. We all thought we'd made it. That we would be one big happy family. He is crushed. I can feel it in him. My heart sinks further. I close my eyes, as one of my tears rolls down my cheek and onto his arm.

Denise, A Week later

Well, life is back to sucking. Sucking severely. Sucking beyond any amount of sucking you've ever known. Living in a house, trying to coexist with someone you know you can't spend your life with, someone that grinds on your nerves even to simply see them. Someone you know can't make you happy. That period of time, just waiting, to be free. To start life on your own. It's a purgatory beyond any other. I feel like a zombie walking through my own home. I just complete the most basic tasks, then go back to sleep. I've been sleeping more and more. It's my only escape. Closing my eyes is the greatest part of my day. To be able to see darkness instead of John's face constantly in my field of vision.

I'm not even talking about when he's actually, physically in front of me. I'm talking about the fact that his face is just always in my minds eye. It's…utterly…and completely… annoying. I don't understand why I deserve this hell on earth. I pacify myself by thinking that this is the time I suffer here on earth. After John and I are divorced, I will be rewarded with life's rewards. Because I have endured so much pain and suffering.

Believe me, I know people suffer physically on this earth, way more than I do here in my own little private hell. I'm not that arrogant. But I tell you, the pain of failed love is real. It is crushing. It messes with your ability to function properly throughout your day. Any little thing - a flower, a restaurant, a photo, a song, especially a song, can just bring you to immediate tears. To think you had it, true love, then it morphs into an evil hag and laughs at you for ever having believed. You are taunted constantly. You see couples hand in hand, and your overly negative, sour attitude just scoffs at any sort of display of love that you might see. You just know it will end in agony. You stop believing in love, and, when that happens, you lose the entire reason for being here.

So yes, people suffer physically, and my heart goes out to them. I wish I could fix every single one of them. But the pain and agony of being alone in the world, not having or believing in true love, it takes its toll on you. It's beyond a broken heart. It's a dark heart, one that doesn't believe any more. One that loses purpose. What is life, when you have a heart with no purpose?

Tonight I had dinner with Amber and Molly in the kitchen. John and Andrew had dinner with each other in the dining room. This is what we are reduced to. The girls can't help themselves, they have to ask. I understand, I can't blame them. This was our dinner conversation:

Amber: "So Mom, there's no hope? None? It's so hard to understand that everything was so perfect, we were all having so much fun, then the next day it's all over?"

Me: "I know honey, it's very difficult to switch gears. From having it all one day, then have nothing the next. I'm so sorry. We just really depended on that love seat. It…it 'fixed' us. It let us see the love for each other."

Molly: "Mom, maybe there's another piece of furniture out there that could do the same thing! You just need to find it!"

I smiled at Molly's suggestion.

Me: "Hmm…you think Dad and I should drive around town to every furniture store and sit together on every piece of furniture in Los Angeles?"

Molly frowned.

Molly: "Well, it would be better than this."

Me: "Awww, honey I know it would. It's just, there's a lot of furniture out there. We could spend the rest of our lives looking for another 'love seat'. I think it's impossible."

I made a sad face at her. I understood how bad she wanted something that would fix this.

Amber: "And you don't feel any of those feelings towards Dad anymore? You can't be happy, feel love for him? Nothing?"

Me: "Amber, it's so so so strange. The minute I saw that love seat gone, every happy, positive feeling for your dad, just left. It vanished. I knew that only minutes before, I had felt love for him."

I looked at Molly.

Me: "I knew we had a great time at your play! One of the best nights EVER!"

Molly smiled. :)

Me: "But, the love seat does something to us. It allows us to see…the love between us I guess."

We all just sat there looking at our plates of taco salad. No one ate. I separated my black beans. Molly mashed her guacamole even more. Amber flicked the tortilla strips over to one side. If any of us could just think of a solution…but we couldn't. It was beyond all of us. Impossible. The only answer is the love seat, and that isn't happening. We all know it. Taco salad had never been so depressing.

John

We have been reduced to dividing the house, rooms, areas, and even kids up. I had dinner with Andrew tonight. I wish to God we could talk about something else, rather than the missing love seat, but it's the only topic anyone cares to talk about. I sift through the taco salad on my plate. Denise's taco salad.

I used to love this. I'm lucky I got any. Andrew grabbed me a portion before Denise could say anything. She likes me to make my own food. She told the kids it was "good practice" for when I'm on my own. So sad, what we are, compared to what we were a short time ago.

God I wish I knew what it was about that love seat, that let us see our love. Let us feel right with each other. Perfect. If we only knew, we could replicate it. At least try. At least feel like we were in a tiny bit of control with this thing. So helpless.

Andrew: "Dad, you don't feel anything towards Mom anymore? You don't love her? At all?"

I speared one black olive on my fork from the taco salad and just looked at it for about thirty seconds before answering.

Me: "Andrew, the best I can explain is I *know* I loved your mom. I *remember* that I felt that way. I remember the conversations, the fun we had just sitting on that stupid love seat. But, that's the problem, they're just memories. Like you remembering that you were excited when you were two, and you got that totally pimped out trike. You remember that you were excited about it, that you loved it, but you don't actually *feel* that excitement in you at this moment. How do you get in touch with that excitement? About a trike? How do you feel that again?

Andrew dropped his head. Stared into his taco salad, untouched except for the salsa he'd moved to the side. He hates salsa. He thought for a while.

Andrew: "But Dad, Mom isn't a trike. She's the woman you married. The love of your life."

Wow. Those words touched me. Chills ran up my spine. I felt what he said. I felt a spark.

Me: "…not a trike, she's the love of my life…" I dropped my fork.

I felt it again. A twinge. A warmth. I immediately got up and briskly walked to the kitchen. I barged into the room. I had no self-control. The tiny spark of warmth took over my actions.

Me: "Denise, you're not a trike, you're the love of my life!"

The look on the faces of Molly, Amber and Denise was one of utter shock. After Molly and Amber processed what I said, they got a slight smile on their face. I looked to Denise. Her face went from shock…to…utter disgust.

Denise: "Not a trike? What the crap! Yes, it's true, I am NOT a trike you brilliant pig ass pork belly'ed crap idiot! What the hell are you doing in here! GET OUT!"

Me: "I…I…"

Andrew: "Mom! You're the love of his life!"

Andrew was so desperate, it was pitiful. My heart broke. I grabbed him and started leading him back to the living room.

Denise: "We are only living in this house John because YOU agreed to the rules! Keep the hell out of my areas! I mean it ass jerk wad!"

Gotta hand it to Denise. The woman has more "ass insults" than anyone I know. Andrew and I got back to the dining room table. We kind of shrugged our shoulders at each other and shared a moment of bitter defeat.

Me: "Sorry kiddo. We tried. It's interesting that I felt something. I felt a twinge of something when you said Mom was the love of my life. Unfortunately, it's not enough to fix us. Little twinges here and there, just not enough. We need that stupid love seat. It sucks because I think we were on the right track. I think we were making progress. I couple of months more, having time off of it, we might have been able to wean ourselves off of it. It just left too soon. We didn't have enough time. "

Andrew didn't look convinced. I knew in his brain he was still trying to figure things out. Find a solution. In his 12 year old mind, he really thought he could find a solution. God, I love that kid. Just then the phone rang. It was sitting on the table next to us, so I picked it up.

Denise

As if my life couldn't get any worse. First John comes running into the kitchen, saying I'm the love of his life? I'm not a trike? Seriously, what the heck did that mean? And was that supposed to be a compliment? "You're not a crumpet, you're the love of my life." "You're not a pancreas, you're the love of my life". What. The. Hell. He's got mental issues.

What? Did he think I would fall all over him? Telling me I'm not a trike? Wow, what a charmer. Suddenly I picture the final rose being given out. There they are, over looking the ocean. Ryan gets down on one knee. Way too much sunlight on them. The wind keeps blowing the bachelorette's hair into her sticky lipstick lips. She has to keep taking it off her lips strand by strand. Chris Harrison is standing in the background.

Ryan: "Trista, you are not a carburetor, you are the love of my life."

Trista can't hold back the tears. She chokes and her cheeks are immediately wet, stained with salty water streaks. Her mascara starts to run. She is shaking.

Trista: "Ryan, you are not a loaf of zucchini bread..."

I shake myself out of the daydream. What a dumb ass bonehead thing to say to me. Urgh. That man.

John

I hang up the phone. I can't hide my excitement.

Andrew: "What dad? What is it?"

Me: "Get your jacket Andrew. We need to leave now."

I run back into that kitchen, burst open the door.

Me: "Denise don't say one word. Girls, Denise, get your coats, we are leaving now! The police found all our things. We need to meet them right now at a storage unit to identify everything. NOW. We leave now!"

I don't even wait for her response. I just get the car keys and go straight out to the car. I sit there for exactly thirty two seconds before everyone is out of that house and in the car. No one speaks the entire ride. We all share our secret, unspoken hope. It is huge hope. I can't help but think that the love seat just *has* to be there. It's completely worthless to anyone but Denise and I. If I can look in that storage unit and see only the love seat, I would be the happiest man on earth. I'm not a super religious man, but all I can say in my head the entire ride is, "Please God please..."

Denise

I've always believed in miracles. I've always believed that either angels, or people that work directly for God (whatever God that may be), are here on earth doing their amazing work. Sometimes, things just happen, and you just *know* it didn't happen through a regular, normal human process. That there's just no way it could have been possible without some intervention from a higher power.

I also have no problem in believing in psychic abilities and even some magic here and there. I am not basing my thoughts on the "you only use 10% of your brain theory." I don't even know if that's true or not. I think some people I've met use a lot more than 10% of their brains…and likewise…some people I've met are clearly running at the 1% or lower mark. So no, brain power is not what convinces me some people have psychic power, or that there is magic happening here on this earth.

What *does* convince me, are those "moments". The moments in life that there is no explanation for. When something happens, combined with that feeling deep down that there is no logical explanation or proof for what just happened. The moment where a mother suddenly knows her child is hurt. I actually had an asthma attack once, out on a bike ride. I was with my brother and dad, but they had gone ahead. I couldn't breathe. I was gasping and walking my bike back to the house. My mom came racing down the street, running, because she knew something was wrong.

I have my fair share of psychic moments. Once John and I were in the drive through at El Pollo Loco. He said, "Ok, guess what the name of the girl at the drive through window is." I didn't even think about it. I immediately said "Leticia". Not the most common name. And yes, her name was Leticia. We were pretty much screaming and freaking out when we got to the window. I never *try* to be psychic. It just happens. I can't control when or where it happens, it just does. I would love to have more control over it, but then again, would I? That could be pretty revealing and frightening at times.

I am fairly certain that this call from the police is a miracle. A gift from God. To us. So we can live happily ever after. I actually smile on the way to the storage unit. I turn to look at the kids. Every single one of them has a smile on their face. Even Molly, in the very back. (The child who has to sit in the third row seating usually is very unhappy in our family. Not sure if that's the way it works in all families, but there is a LOT of fighting over who has to sit in the very back. Sheesh...kids. *Eye roll)

We pull up to the storage units. I am surprised to see it is just regular public storage units, like on *Storage Wars*. How sad if the police didn't find our things, and we were watching *Storage Wars* one day, and saw Dan Dotson auctioning off all our possessions. I find that show really depressing. Those are things that are meaningful to someone, somewhere in time. At some point, the table they label as "worthless" had a family sitting around it for a holiday dinner. It's amazing to me that the things we cherish during our lifetime become junk in the next lifetime.

I have never seen John move so quickly. He turns off the car, takes the key out, opens the car door and is out of the car all in one movement. It all happens at once. Yes, it is not humanly possible, but I'm telling you, that's exactly what he does. I don't feel any hatred towards him, I just feel...anticipation, I guess. I am very nervous. So nervous. I am shaking and slightly sweating under my hair on the back of my neck.

The kids and I get out of the car. Andrew goes running up with John while Molly and Amber each take a hand of mine. I am squeezing their hands so tight, I actually picture squeezing their fingers completely off. Walking Dead much? It is a horrid daydream, so I just loosen my grip a tiny bit. Look, I can't help the thoughts in my head. You should know that by now. You can't and shouldn't judge me. So don't look at me like that. (See? Psychic. I knew you were looking at me funny!)

We are all standing in front of the police officers outside the storage unit.

Officer: "Hello everyone, didn't expect the whole family to come, but I can understand you all are pretty excited to get your things back, huh?"

Andrew: "Yes we are!"

Molly: "OPEN IT!!!"

The police officers laugh.

Officer: "Ok everyone, we don't want you to touch anything yet," (he looks at Molly) "so if there are any of your favorite stuffed animals in there, you can't go grab them, OK?"

Molly frowns at him.

Molly: "I don't care about any stupid stuffed animals, I just want the love seat back!"

The officer's eyebrows raise and he looks at his partner.

Officer: "Love seat? Well, that must be a very comfortable love seat."

Both officers chuckle.

Molly: "Please! Can you just open that!"

The officer looks at this demanding ten year old like two feet below him.

Officer: "Alrighty then, let's get to it. You can't touch anything, we will need to have everything fingerprinted, see if there's any evidence in there. Right now we just want to identify the stolen property, see if this is all yours, OK?"

All of us say "OK" at once. So embarrassing when that happens, and you seem like some freaky robot family.

The officer walks to the storage door and rolls it up. My mouth drops open. Not because I see the love seat, but because every single thing is packed perfectly. Rubber protectors on every corner of tables, dressers. Padding around chairs. Things are packed and taped in boxes with bubble wrap, peanuts, etc. Moving blankets are placed between things so nothing would be scratched. Things are perfectly packed. So much care has gone into packing all our things. I can't process what kind of criminal would do this. I literally bring my hand to my head and scratch. It doesn't help though, I am still baffled.

I think John is as confused as me at the pristine packing job. Neither of us notice Molly crying.

Officer: "What's wrong little lady? Don't see your love seat?"

That snaps John and I out of it. I don't see it! NO! It isn't here? I start to rush into the storage unit to get a better look. It *must* be here! No way would every single thing be here except the love seat! The officer grabs my arm and prevents me from heading in.

Officer: "I'm really sorry, you can't go in there. The forensics team will be here in just a couple of minutes."

Me: "It has to be there!"

John: "They didn't rob our house just to take that love seat! No way!"

Officer: "What was so special about this love seat? Antique?"

None of us answer. We all know there was no answering that question. We are the only people in the world who know what that love seat meant to us. I feel such despair at this moment. But then I look at the kids. Dear god. This is painful. They look…hopeless. You never want to see your kids looking hopeless. : (

Me: "I can't really tell what's going on behind those boxes to the right. It's possible it could be there. I just don't understand why they would pack up these things so nicely, I mean were they going to sell them? Ok, but why everything but the love seat?"

Officer: "Well, if you all seemed to like it so much, maybe other people saw how great it was too."

This is a surprise. John and I glance at each other. Oh wow. What if. What if the love seat worked for someone else! Never thought of that. It could be. Maybe. Maybe not. Who knows. Who cares. The forensic people come, there isn't one fingerprint on anything in the whole storage unit. When they take all the plastic and blankets off the furniture, all they find are our own fingerprints on our own furniture. Who would go to so much trouble? It makes no sense at all. But who ever did this really screwed up our lives. I hate them. I want to rip them apart. It's so not fair that they took away our happiness. Our only shot.

John

Found all of our possessions. No love seat. We got all our things back a couple of days ago. I really feel, just…vacant. I just have nothing. I don't have anything, words, thoughts that actually *mean* anything. I'm just blank. I don't care. I just want this all to end. The only time I have a glimmer of hope is when I think of the life that is to come for me. A life, with my own place. No Denise. I'm convinced that she sucks every bit of hope and happiness from the air in this house. There is nothing left for me.

I heard from the attorney about the timeline. When everything will happen. I decide to go talk to her. She is in the bedroom as usual. She never comes out of that damn room except for dinner. I open the door. She is on the bed, on her laptop, which she closes abruptly when I enter.

Denise: "What the hell John, maybe you could knock? That would be nice!"

Me: "I did knock Denise."

Yeah, I say that "Denise" with as much spite and ugly sarcasm as I can.

Denise: "You knock, then you wait to be invited in. You do not knock and then immediately just enter. So fucking rude."

John: "I really don't care if you think I'm rude, or what you think of me. The reason I came up here is to let you know what the attorney said."

Denise: "Excellent, you'll be leaving soon?"

John: "Not soon enough. It's April, and I was wondering if for the kids' sakes, you have any desire to wait until they get out of school for the summer to finalize this and sell the house, or...would you like to do it right now?"

Denise's mood changes. I can see it. But I don't know what mood she changes to. I can just tell she suddenly looks different. She taps her fingers over and over on her laptop. Just keeps tapping. She doesn't ever look up at me again. She finally speaks, still looking down at her laptop.

Denise: "Yeah, that's great. As soon as the kids get out of school we will put the house up for sale, and finalize the divorce. Great. Now get out."

I take one last look at her sitting there. Looking down, tapping on the laptop. I open my mouth to say something, but nothing comes out. I feel strange. Depressed. Cold.

I just want to sit in a dark room and listen to sad music. I go downstairs back to the guest room and plug into my iPhone. First off is "Plenty" by Sarah Mc Lachlan. Nice, sad song.

No matter what they'd say, I would have thought I'd be with you
until my dying day.

267

Denise

John just left my room. I sit staring at the door he closed for about thirty minutes. He wasn't just closing the door to our bedroom, he was closing the door to our marriage. This is the end. Our last days living in a house together. I'm surprised at my melancholy state. I mean, I know inside, we can't be together. I don't want to be with him. I detest him. What I'm surprised at is that I feel all the sadness and gloom surrounding our impending divorce. How do you feel depressed about divorcing a man you can't stand? I'm very confused. I feel all out of sorts. I feel like every part of my body belongs to someone else. That my arm is not mine. My hand is not mine. My eyes aren't mine. I'm just a bunch of glued together body parts. I'm not me. My brain is even pieced together. My thoughts aren't right. Part of me hates John, yet part of me is heartbroken we are actually ending this.

Suddenly the world shifts again, fog starts rushing past me, I feel dizzy. I lay back on the bed to participate in my spectacular daydream. It's daytime, but there is a considerable amount of fog. Which is weird, because you really never see fog hovering around the ground in the San Gabriel Valley in Los Angeles. Pasadena just isn't England, now matter how you slice it. I see Molly's school through the fog. Then I begin to make out children, running, screaming in every direction. Mothers are racing to their children, picking them up in a panic. Clutching them in their arms, running and screaming. I see some locking themselves with random kids they've grabbed around them into their cars. Everyone is panic stricken, frightened out of their wits. I can't comprehend what they are freaking out about. I am moving so slowly, almost limping along. One of my feet seems to drag on the mist covered ground. I make my way up to the office to try to see what's going on and to find Molly.

I catch a glimpse of myself in the glass door...I'm a...monster. All the parents and children are running from *me*! I can see the seams and stitches where I've been sewn together. There is old, dried, crusted blood at my stitches holding me together. My head is misshapen and flattish on top. I try to speak to tell Molly's friend Allison, who is running past me, try to tell her that it's OK, it's just me, Mrs. Hughes...but no words come out. Just a loud moan "Ahhhhh uhhhhhh." Allison screams at the top of her lungs and runs away.

I hear laughing. Horrible, evil, laughter. I turn in the direction of the laughter and through the dense fog, I see John, standing there in a lab coat. Dr. Ass Frankenstein. Laughing and laughing, and laughing. I stumble and fall, crawling towards him. He just keeps laughing. I can't take it any more. I open my eyes. That is SO something John would do! Transform me into a monster then just laugh about it. Ugh. What a punk ass jerk!

I have never felt more low or depressed in my entire life. Only one thing to do. I open iTunes and go to my special, sad, makes-me-cry-every-time-I-listen-to-these-songs playlist. I click on "Love on the Rocks" by Neil Diamond…then I cry. I cry so hard.

Gave you my heart.
Gave you my soul.
You left me alone here
with nothing to hold.
Yesterday's gone.
Now all I want is a smile.

First, they say they want you.
How they really need you.
Suddenly you find you're out there,
Walking in the storm.

When they know they have you,
Then they really have you.
Nothing you can do or say
You've got to leave, just get away,
We all know the song.

Bad break up songs are my guilty pleasure. John always made fun of me for liking songs like this. "Against All Odds" by Phil Collins. "Broken Wings" by Mister Mister. "Do You Really Want To Hurt Me" by Culture Club. "Missing You" by John Waite. I can't help it. Those songs just get me. Yes, I'm aware they're some really terrible music, but when you're sad and you *want* to cry, they are very helpful. I can't really put on Korn or Slipknot and just start crying. It takes those old, bad, sappy love songs. They just don't make them like that anymore.

I sit here listening to music, crying for a long time. I have completely lost track of the time when Amber opens the door. "If I Could Turn Back Time" by Cher is playing and I am just adding another tissue to my huge pile that has accumulated during my sad song fest.

Amber: "Mom? It's 7:00 o'clock. Are you going to make dinner?"

Urgh. I'm doing it again. I'm sitting here wallowing in my own misery. Forgetting my kids. Forgetting anything that matters. Forgetting I have a life. I can't do this! I have to stay in control. I can't let him suck every ounce of life from me!

Me: "Amber, I'm sorry, I was just having a moment, but I'm good now. I'm OK. I'll be down in just a second and start dinner."

I smile at her as best I can. She smiles back and closes the door. I'm not going to let him win. God help me I will become the best actor this world has ever seen. I will not sit on this bed day after day, crying my life away. I had my cry. I'm good to go. Time to start living!

I get up, do ten jumping jacks to get the blood flowing, and scoop all the tissues into the wastebasket. I put some make-up on. Put on some real clothes, not just the mom sweats I've been in for three days, and go downstairs to make dinner. Yes! This is a new me. One good cry to crappy music is all it took. Crappy music therapy. Thank God for crappy music.

John, Easter Sunday March 31st 6:00 a.m.

What is up with that funky nut? And when I say "funky nut", I'm talking about Denise. She has started dressing like a Rastafarian. Not even kidding. She isn't brushing her hair or something. It's just twisted in all these little wads. I don't really think white, PTA moms actually have the right type of hair for dreadlocks, but go tell her that, will you? She wears this knit cap, red, yellow and green. It was Andrew's when he went as a hippie for Halloween three years ago. She wears this long flowing floral muumuu just about every day. I wouldn't be surprised if she's up there with a big fatty every night. (Ok, I have to admit. I actually had to 'urban dictionary' that, because I only call it pot and apparently no one calls pot pot anymore. Sucks being old.)

But…the weirdest things is…she hasn't been raging at me, mean to me, hasn't said one rude thing to me. She is just always moving. It's really unsettling. It's not like "Denise" at all. She's going to the market, she's doing laundry, she's looking at houses to rent, she's taking the kids to school, she's helping with homework, or she's watching TV with the kids. She never complains. Actually, she's the perfect mom. The perfect Rastafarian mother?

Today is a busy day. It's Easter Sunday. I talked with Lady Shoshanna a couple of weeks ago and we decided to make this last Easter together with the kids a great one. (I should explain. I went to this "reggae name generator" online, put in Denise's name and voila! Her "reggae name" is Lady Shoshanna. So that's what I have been calling her. She doesn't seem to mind.

We never go to church, especially me, since I'm Jewish. But, we thought it would be nice to go to church with Denise's parents and the kids on Easter Sunday, then have a nice brunch here after church with some egg hunting for the kids. As Jewish as I am, we have always had egg hunts for the kids. Me... Jew man, actually gets up at 5 a.m. to put gifts, candy and eggs in the yard before the kids wake up. I've even left trails of cotton balls that went all the way down the street and out to the highway. Let a Jew loose with a holiday that they've seen their whole life growing up and never got to participate in, this is what happens. We go a little crazy. You should see our Christmas tree / Chanukah bush. I'll miss all those kooky Christian traditions. I'll miss being able to do this, for the kids, as a family.

Today will be a little tricky. The plan is for me to leave church a bit early, work call, computer issue, so I can get back before everyone and put out all the eggs. Andrew knows there is no Easter Bunny. Amber holds into that idea of the Easter Bunny like a mother holding

273

a newborn baby. That girl will be forty before she even thinks about letting go of the Easter Bunny idea. And Molly still believes in the Easter Bunny. So this is her Easter.

Denise, Easter Sunday 11:00 a.m. Church

All I can do is look down at my phone and type. On one hand, I am really happy that we are at church with the kids. I think how nice it would be if we'd done that every year. You don't have to believe 100% in everything a church teaches, but just having your family together like this, it's just really nice. I'm having an issue with "him" being one person over however. It's irritating me. I can "sense" him. Even if I am looking the other direction. I feel thoughts coming off of him. Judging me. Judging my muumuu.

My dad is on the end of the pew, then Andrew, Amber, my mom, me, Molly then John. John's head is above Molly's, so I have a clear view. I hate the shape of that man's head. It's just too round or something. And greasy. It's like he works at In-N-Out Burger. Have you seen those people that work there? They're all so sweaty in that tiny little space. Burger steam giving them meat facials all day long. Gross.

The service starts and Father Laurence comes into the church walking down the center aisle. Followed by altar boys and girls. The people doing the readings and then the choir. The altar kids carry a big cross with a white sheet over it. There always has to be that mysterious sheet that Jesus left behind. Personally, if I arose from death after hanging on a cross for the weekend, I'd take that sheet with me. I'm fairly modest though, call me crazy. Maybe Jesus was an

275

exhibitionist? Who knows. I just know that Jesus didn't arise to a pile of laundered clothing sitting in his tomb and that sheet could have come in very handy.

Everything goes OK. Dad only falls asleep about eight times. I give Andrew the look, and he nudges Dad, just as Dad's chin reaches his chest. Mom keeps fixing Amber's outfit. I can tell it is driving Amber crazy, but she doesn't say anything. Just keeps looking straight ahead. I can tell my mom wants to fix the lady's outfit in front of us also. The woman's tag is sticking out over her pants. Size 14. Cotton and Polyester blend. Machine wash with like colors. My mom just keeps looking at that tag and twitches.

We make it through the whole mass and it is time for communion. Honest to god, I don't know what happens after that. I remember standing and screaming something. I remember my dad pulling me out of the church. I remember walking through the front door. My favorite muumuu is somehow soaked with holy water. Everything else is a blur.

Next thing I know I am back in my room, on my bed and my mom is sitting in a chair next to me.

Mom: "Honey? How are you feeling? Better?"

I look around the room to get my bearings. It's really confusing to have these lapses. It's like I'm having an alcohol induced blackout, but worse, because I don't get to drink. I take a minute and replay everything I remember so I can catch myself up to reality.

Me: "I know I started yelling in church, and Dad dragged me out. Now I'm here. That's about all I can recall."

I look questioningly at my mom and give her a shoulder shrug that says, "OK, fill in the blanks."

Mom: "Well, you started screaming 'HE'S A JEW. JEWISH SPY. A JEW AMONG US.' "

My jaw drops. I am horrified. How could I have gone from being so IN control to so OUT of control? Oh my god.

Mom: "Then, as you got to the holy water, you cupped it in your hands and kept throwing it at him."

Me: "Seriously??????"

Mom nods her head. I gasp in horror and put my hands over my mouth. Dear God. What is wrong with me. I immediately feel tears in my eyes. This isn't fair. That I can't even control my words. My actions. My life is just basically maintaining until I go off on John again. Now, every single Catholic person in our community knows I'm a freak and that John is a Jew spy. Ugh. That affects the kids too. Why me? What did I do to deserve this life? A life with a miserable marriage and no control over myself, It's like I'm actually trying to make everyone hate me.

Me: "Why? Why would I do that Mom?"

Mom: "Honey, I don't know. I know you dislike John. But, he must have done something horrible to you for you to want to hurt him so badly."

I immediately make a face at my mom. Crinkle my nose and eyes as if to say, "What are you talking about!" It makes me mad in a weird way.

Me: "Mom, he hasn't done anything to me!"

I catch myself as soon as I say that. Her eyebrows go up into her hairline. I understand how unbelievable that sounds to her.

Mom: "Honey, maybe you need to see someone. A psychologist? Just someone to run all this past. I'm not an expert. I don't know why you seem to hate him one minute, can't stand him, and then the next, you are defending him. I think we're all confused. I think the kids are ready Denise. They're ready to move on from this place. I don't think they can take much more."

Me: "Mom, we are just waiting until school is out. Just like a month and a half. Then we are selling the house and moving into separate apartments. I already found mine. I'm putting a deposit on it next week. I don't want to put them through anything Mom. Don't you understand? I have no control over it. It just happens. I don't *want* it to happen. I hate it. I'm miserable. I'm so sick of being miserable."

I bury my head in my bent knees and cry. I cry so hard that my mom actually is forced to be a normal mom and comfort me. She uncomfortably moves herself to where she is semi-sitting-squatting on the edge of the bed. Her hand hovers for about thirty seconds, not knowing what to do. She then pats me on the shoulder.

Mom: "Honey, we'll get this sorted out. Once you are not living with John anymore, I'm just certain your life will be better. I know it. We have to get rid of that man."

Well, she tried. Her solution to everything is simply getting rid of John. Then the world will be back on track. Sigh. Mom.

John, later that evening

Wow. Well, I'm pretty sure that was my last mass. I'm not so sure that St. Anthony's Catholic Church will want the "Jew spy" back among their parishioners. I'm not exactly positive who I'm working for. Which group of Jewish people really need to know what goes on behind the scenes at a catholic service? THAT is the question. Jews that infiltrate Catholic masses for the purpose of...ummmmm...ideas for sermons? A closer look at the Eucharist? Maybe the Jews are trying to figure out how the hell those damn Catholics actually turn that good wine into blood. Crazy Catholics. A bunch of vampires if you ask me. Every Sunday hundreds of thousands of people drinking blood? WTH.

Well, Denise has really done a number this time. She embarrassed our entire family in front of the entire community. I noticed April Miller, Denise's favorite PTA mom, laughing as Denise's dad pulled Denise out of the church. This has to stop. We need to move forward now. I'm done. No way in hell am I putting myself or my children through this anymore. It stops today.

Denise's parents make Easter dinner for the kids. I sit and eat a little with them, but mainly I just feel sick. I help Denise's dad clean the kitchen while her mom goes upstairs and talks to her.

After they leave, I decide to tell Denise I am moving out tomorrow. That this is it. No more. I stand up to head upstairs, when the door to the guest room opens. It's Denise.

She stands in my doorway for a few seconds, before she enters and closes the door.

Denise: "John…"

My heart breaks in this moment. It is already cracked down the center. But, seeing her there, standing in the guest room, struggling for words…it is simply too much. My heart cracks in two. We both know what is coming. Know what needs to be done.

Denise: "John, I'm sorry."

She lookes down. God, that had to be so hard for her.

Me: "Denise, it's not like you have control over it. I know in a perfect world, you wouldn't do or say those things to me."

Denise: "I wouldn't. I have no control John. I must be so much weaker than you. I'm truly sorry."

I muster an ever so slight smile. The last thing I want to do is smile, believe me, but I just have to try. For her. To try to make her feel the tiniest bit better. I feel how hard this is for her. I feel it.

Denise: "I wouldn't purposely hurt you. I just don't know why, being off the love seat, I just seem to have nothing but meanness inside me. I can't do anything but hurt you, hurt the kids. I disappoint everyone. I just can't help but believe if I'm not living in the same location as you, then I wouldn't do these horrible things. You could be...happy."

Me: "Denise, this isn't all your fault. Believe me, if I could come up with a solution, a way to simulate being on the love seat, I would. In a heartbeat. But, it just seems so hopeless. We can't get the love seat back, and we certainly can't go on living like this."

Denise: "No, we can't."

She looks down, and I just continue to look at her. Her hands fidgeting. A big clump of hair swinging across one eye. My wife. This is a painful moment for us. The moment that we know we have exhausted every solution. The moment we know there is nothing left. There is no more trying. No more effort. No more tears. It's just gone. Over. She looks up at me. She has some big pools of tears sitting in those blue eyes of hers. Knowing that the person you've spent most of your life with isn't the one you will spend your last days with, is so tragic.

She can't speak. She just gives the tiniest smile, sweeps the big clump of hair out of her eye, and leaves my room.

It's such a strange time. I understand there is no "us". We are over. We have no relationship. No future together. At our kid's graduations, weddings, having babies, Denise and I will be there, but we will be separate. Living our own lives. We'll probably both be with other people... "other people". Wow. Denise with another man. I've always teased her about Trent Reznor and Alan Rickman. (I know she only likes Alan Rickman as Professor Snape because he actually looks like Trent Reznor in the Perfect Drug video.) But, to actually think of her with another man. I let out an audible chuckle. Not that I find it amusing or funny in the least. Because I find it horrifying. Horrible.

At that moment my door opens. It's Molly. She hands me an envelope.

Molly: "Dad I forgot, this came in the mail yesterday. From my play."

She sounds very monotone and not happy. I can't blame her. Her play was such a great night. Every single one of us were convinced that night was the cornerstone. The night that showed us not only was it possible to be off the love seat and have a life, but the night that showed us that Denise and I were in love. We knew. It was so clear.

I open the envelope. It is an 8 x 10 photo of all of us. Denise's parents, the kids, Molly in her costume, and Denise and I, with our arms around each other. They had one of the dads there taking photos for a fundraiser and we had ordered one. I can't tell you how long I stare at that photo. It's from a different time. Yet, when I look at the photo, I feel it. I feel the happiness we felt on that night. I feel Denise. I look at my arms, I have goosebumps all over them. I close my eyes as tight as I possibly can, then open them again and look at the photo. There it is. All of it. I can see it. See how I felt about Denise. See the love we had for each other. I can *see* her. Her heart. How she felt about me. My head is spinning.

I grab the photo and run out of my room. The kids all look at me bleakly as I sprint up the stairs. I can't stop to say anything to them. Denise has to see this photo NOW!

Denise

I don't feel better. I'll never feel better. This has all gone so wrong. This just isn't how I saw my life going when I was sixteen years old. I saw my future as so bright. All the things I wanted to accomplish. I wanted to be an artist. I wanted to write. I just knew I'd have a successful marriage. I'd never make the mistakes other people made. Never. I'd never just become complacent and boring like so many other couples. I knew better. I was so sure, so confident.

Now I look at the mess before me. I've done nothing I wanted to do in life. Not one thing. Well I got married and had kids, but it's gone nothing like I planned it. My kids are great, but I chose wrong. I've brought three children into a hopeless marriage. Now they will be children from a broken home. They will be those typical kids with two moms and two dads. John…with another woman. Married to another woman. Suddenly a pit grows in my gut. This just isn't what I planned.

Who are the lucky ones? The ones whose lives actually go according to plan. Who are the people that pick someone at age 25 and actually stay with that person until they die? Together forever? Is that even possible? I guess it is, I mean people do celebrate fiftieth wedding anniversaries. I just feel like it's so rare. Like winning the lottery. Who you are at twenty five is so hugely different from who you are at forty five. Everything changes. What you like to do. What you think is funny. The music you like. The food you eat. If everything changes, how *do* you find someone at twenty five that you will still have everything in common with at forty five?

At that moment John comes bounding into my room. In one jump he goes from the door to bouncing on my bed and shoving a photo in front of my face. Instantly I am irritated with him. I hate when people don't knock, no respect for privacy, or simply no respect. I frown at him ready to start screaming I'm sure, when I look down at the photo.

It's us. Our family. Mom and Dad. The kids. From the night of Molly's play. My frown lessens. I can't help it. Involuntarily the corners of my mouth turn ever so slightly upward. My head twitches. I glance at John, but quickly look back to the photo. I can't look at him. He is just sitting there, relaxed looking. Smiling at me. He looks so happy. I have to admit, I am really liking the feeling I have when I look at the photo. It was somehow this magical night. Yes it ended in tragedy, but, still. That night. So happy. Such a great time as a family. As a couple.

My smile broadens on my face. I can not help it! I try. Part of me doesn't want to succumb to the smile and happiness that John is experiencing. But here again I am experiencing that oh so familiar feeling of not having control over my own body. I feel a warmth tingle over my skin, replacing the coldness. I close my eyes for a moment to try to appreciate every tiny bit of warmth as it spreads over me. It feels so good. I feel so...

I open my eyes and look at John.

Me: "What is this John? What's happening?"

John: "Just keep looking at the photo, please."

I look back to the photo and smile bigger. Us. John and I. I see it. I feel it. I know it. John and I need to be together. Always. I look back at him, smiling so big at me.

Me: "Is this photo like the love seat? When we look at it, everything is OK?"

John laughs and tosses the photo across the room.

John: "Nope. Not like the love seat at all. The photo is over there Denise."

He nods in the direction of the photo laying face down on the carpet about ten feet away.

John: "So, do you hate me?"

I look at the photo. I look back to him. I actually feel my left arm with my right hand, to see if I can feel that warmth. Oh, I feel it. I am like burning up with warmth and wonderful feelings. I smile at him.

Me: "John, I don't hate you at all."

John: "I know right!!!"

He jumps towards me and hugs me. I close my eyes. I can't even hug him back. I have no energy. I don't have one muscle in my body. I'm just a lump of warmth and happiness. I just feel his embrace with this goofy smile on my face. His arms around me. I shiver at the feeling of having his arms around me. Not a "cold" shiver. A shiver of absurdly intense happiness. I never want his arms to be any place else but around me. It feels so wonderful.

With my eyes still closed, I speak to him.

Me: "John, what is happening? Why am I feeling this way? What just happened? We looked at a photo and everything is right?"

I am so afraid to open my eyes, as if this feeling might disappear.

John: "Denise, I'm not exactly sure. I feel like, we locked off certain places in our memories over the years. Certain parts of our hearts got locked up. Maybe because we neglected each other. Maybe because we were actually hurt. Maybe because we didn't like each other. I feel like the ability to see each other in a loving way, without the aid of any outside help, was impossible. We had blockage in certain areas of feelings towards each other. The love seat unclogged those blocked areas. I don't really know. But right now, I know, that all that is gone. It's like everything has been unlocked. I'm free. Don't you feel it? Aren't you free now? Can't you tell me with 100% certainty that all those negative feelings are gone for good? They're gone Denise. Open your eyes and see. They're gone."

I open my eyes and look at his arms around me. I smile. I slowly look in his eyes. He is right. Every single negative feeling is gone. All of them. I know it. I am certain of it. I'm not sitting on a love seat. I'm not looking at a photograph. I am sitting on our bed, with John's arms around me and I feel amazing. I look over at the photograph still on the ground.

Me: "So what did looking at that photograph do? I don't get it?"

John chuckles.

John: "Denise, I don't know. Maybe it reminded us? Of what we've always had? Maybe it unlocked the final chamber? Maybe we just snapped out of it? Maybe that one act of seeing ourselves truly happy that night, showed us THAT is the real us. This horrible, sad, pathetic excuse of a couple, that's not us Denise. That is NOT us! Do I need to know exactly what happened here? Do I need to question it for the rest of my life? NO! I just want to thank whatever it is that allowed us to get rid of those horrible feelings towards each other. Thank it for letting me just live my days with you. Day after day Denise. Always. You and me. 'Til the end. This is it."

I finally find some muscle and put my arms around him. We eventually just fall over. We never move from this tight embrace all night. We just sleep in our clothes, pressed right against each other. Arms locked

around each other. In the middle of the bed. All night.
:)

Denise, 1 year later

I haven't even thought about formulating my thoughts about John and I in a very long time. I haven't needed to. Turns out, this is a happy ending. This story didn't end like so many other marriages in the world. We won that lottery. After looking at that photograph from the night of Molly's play, we never turned back. Never felt any of those negative thoughts whatsoever. It just ended. We didn't need a love seat to show us the way. We simply needed each other. Our relationship from that point on has been amazing. We have walked hand in hand everywhere we go. There is no fighting. We are one. Almost like our brains have been fused together. We finish each other's sentences. We just seem to agree on everything, from where to eat, to how do deal with the kids, and what to watch on TV. We have way too much fun for "married people"!

I can't tell you how often I think about the fact that we came THIS close to giving it all up. Because we didn't see it? We didn't feel it? We have had some long talks into the night about this. It breaks my heart, every time I hear of someone getting a divorce now. Breaking up. I don't care if it's a celebrity couple, or a couple at our kids' school. A couple that's been together for 8 months or 20 years. It always affects me in such a tremendous way now.

Personally, I still feel that love seat held some sort of magic. It just had to. We were destined for divorce.

There was no turning back. But after it appeared in our house, and after we sat on it of course, then we saw the truth. I can't explain to you the feeling that I felt when I sat on that piece of furniture. I think John has forgotten the sensation, but I haven't. I never will. It just wasn't normal. It wasn't of this earth. Nothing you would feel normally. John doesn't think the love seat held any magic at all. He thinks it was just a catalyst. An excuse sort of, a reason to feel how we *actually* felt about each other. He thinks it could have been a pillow, a song, a piece of toast. He thinks we just needed *something* that wasn't us that we could project our feelings into.

I understand what he's saying. I guess he could be right. I do wish I knew. I do wish I could find Tian. His store. But, more than that, I wish to have a happy marriage that will see me into old age. To have someone that would not only be my love, but is my best friend. Someone that I sincerely love to do everything with. From going to the market to going to Italy. Someone that makes me laugh when I'm brushing my teeth, cooking dinner or during mass. Someone that is always there for me, through my mistakes in life, to losing loved ones, to trying to corral teenagers. I got it. I got what I most desired in life. How? Because we were lucky enough to realize what we had.

We were lucky enough to realize that it was *always* there. We were the same people that we were when we first fell in love. All the ideas and feelings were still there. Sure our physical bodies have changed. Sure our situation has changed. YES children change things. Time can be very evil and cruel, it can disguise things. We thought we had nothing left in common. We thought we weren't attracted to each other. We thought we didn't enjoy each other's company, going out to dinner, concerts, shopping. We thought we were different people. That we had evolved in a different direction that the other person. We thought we grew apart.

How many couples in this world think the same thing? That initial spark of love and attraction wears off, and bam. Nothing left. Then the misery begins. Staying together for the kids? You hear that one a lot. Going to therapy. Trying to work things out. Affairs. Marriage in this world is a mess. Why? Because people let the fog in. That fog of time. That fog of the passing years. They let that fog cover their marriage. It's so thick, it covers their feelings. People can't see clearly, what they have. They are convinced that they made a mistake choosing their partner. It's like they completely forget how they once loved that person. Everyone thinks you change *so* much. And you do. Things *do* change over the years. Your situation changes. All of that around you. You have kids. Your financial situation changes. Where you live changes. What I'm saying is, that initial spark of electricity, that initial thing that attracted you to your spouse, is still there. Oh it may be buried under years of macaroni and cheese, bills, spot remover and kids' Tylenol, but it IS still there.

I'm not saying that all people who get divorced are wrong. No. Not at all. Sometimes you have to kick those idiots to the curb. But I am saying that I bet a lot of people who just give up and get divorced, because it's so damn easy to do these days, actually didn't need to.

I think divorce is accepted. I mean if fifty percent of couples get divorced, that's half. (Ha ha, I'm brilliant I know. Fractions were always my forté.) For every couple getting married, one will get divorced. It's acceptable to be divorced. No one will look down on you. We live in a world where it "just happens." People accept that you make mistakes. That who you pick to marry at age twenty five, just doesn't work out. That person changes and meh, maybe it'll work out, maybe not. You can always get divorced and try again.

I'm just saying, I have a little more faith in who people choose the first time. I think finding true love is kind of a one shot deal in this life. I think many, many people have given up their true loves. They have given up to the fog. They let the fog win. They just stopped putting forth any effort. I was ready to give up! I don't know how I lucked out to get that love seat. Maybe something in John and I was still open to the potential that still lived in both of us. WE couldn't see it, but something inside of us still remembered.

I wish all couples with problems could get a love seat of their own. I wish I could give it to them personally. But it doesn't have to be a love seat. It just has to be an openess to what you once had. You can't close the door on the memories. When you were first together - you have to be able to feel those memories. Feel that love you once had. You *can* get in touch with that again.

You need to get away from the daily grind of hell that we put ourselves through. Who can get in touch with love...when you're busy getting gum out of hair? Dog poop off shoes? Trying to make installment payments with the IRS. Rushing someone to the ER. Rewashing loads of laundry because you failed to put it in the dryer and now it's all mildew smelling sitting in the washing machine. Having the vacuum bag break and it's contents fly all over your freshly vacuumed carpet. I mean who the hell can think about getting in touch with old sweet, love feelings with all that crap going on in life? WHO?

Life sucks and it's crazy hard. What you NEED is a partner. Someone to be there for you. Your fall guy/girl. The one who will always have your back. The one who, when faced with all this day to day shittola we go through, will put their hands on your back and give you a quick one minute massage while whispering in your ear, "Soon we will be in bed watching Jimmy Fallon."

No relationship stays how it was at the beginning. You are either one of those people who will forever be trying to get that "initial sensation" over and over and over again...multiple failed relationships... OR...you will be that person that can see through the fog and stay in touch with the reasons you fell in love with this person. They're still there. That's all I'm trying to tell you. Those feelings that you felt initially, with that person that you can't stand to look at right now, those feelings are still there. But you have to let go of all that hatred. Resentment. Jealousy. Let it go. When you do, the fog will start to lift. Once you see anything through the fog, don't let that go. Any little hint. Spark. Cling to it. Do not give up. It's still there. The feelings. The emotions. The love. It's there.

I will always wonder about the love seat. If it actually had "magical" effects on us. I guess I hope it wasn't magic. I guess I hope John is right. That somehow we just chose the love seat, and used it as a catalyst to be able to feel all the feelings that were still there right in front of us. Deep inside, it was something we both wanted. We just didn't know how to approach it. We had so much hatred at that point in us. If that's the case, if there was no magic involved, then that means that everyone else in this world can have the opportunity that we did. The opportunity to see that the love we once had was still there right under our noses.

I wish people could see. I wish they could stop the momentum once it starts. I wish they could back up. Just sit and start talking about all the memories they can think of from when they first met. When they were first dating. Dancing. Kissing. So much is forgotten and flies out the window as the marriage goes on and dear

God, try adding children to that mix. That is one fucked up brew to chug down. Kids really suck the fun out of a marriage. Blah blah blah, don't even start on me, telling me "children are the most fulfilling part of your life." NO! I do not accept that. They are seriously fucked up little creatures who test you at every corner. OK. They're kind of cute when you dress them up, and they sit there, not speaking. It's just hard to be responsible for small lives, when you're trying to live your own life. Find your own happiness. It's hard. OK damnit, if I'm being super duper honest, I adore my kids. I think however, if your marriage is teetering on the doorstep of divorce, kids just add these dark clouds and flooding to every little situation. But when your marriage is great, kids are pretty bitchen.

:)

Now, it's John and I against the world. NO one comes between us. The kids are screaming, yelling at each other, being sassy and rude to us? We are on the same team now. If it gets too bad, we'll just retreat to our bedroom, close and lock our door. Maybe we'll watch TV, or maybe we'll just hug. But it's us. Together. Forever. No doubt. Not one single, tiny doubt. This is my man. My partner. The one I was always meant to be with. And I'm his girl.

We sit for hours planning out our lives now. We talk and talk and talk. There is not enough time in the day for us to talk to each other and make plans. It's like "life-planning" is our second job. I make lists of places we want to visit. Lists of things we want to do to our house. Lists of restaurants we want to try. Lists of old movies we want to see. When you love someone, there is SO much to do with them!

Please, find your love seat. :) Try. You just may have that perfect person, the one you love. The one you are meant to spend your days with. The one you are meant to grow old with. They might be right there. Right now. Never say never.

I close my eyes. One last daydream can't hurt. I look down. I'm wearing a very skimpy outfit. Backless. High cut skirt in front. I bend over and look, why yes you can see my crotch and it has red, silky underwear on it. I lift up the black lacey skirt to get a better look at this underwear. Oh ewww, it's high wasted and quite thick. What the heck? And I'm wearing nude colored pantyhose and stubby-ish heels. My self inspection is interrupted due to the fact that someone is yelling. "Trent, TRENT! We need you, you're on in three!" I look up to see Trent Reznor and some tall glitzy looking babe running past me. OMG. OH MY GOD! Trent Reznor!!! Wearing a little bolero jacket and jazz dance shoes? Huh? I look around the room, holy crap! Alan Rickman, is here, dressed like an 80's hairband rocker in black and white checkered pants, a purple Adam and the Ants pirate-y shirt and a red sweatband around his forehead, with his date in an equally bitchen 80's outfit. To my right is Andy Garcia, wearing jeans tucked into cowboy boots, a red & white checked shirt and a bandana over his face also standing with someone dressed the same as him. But as you know, I have a connection to Andy. I'd recognize him rolled up in a blanket behind frosted glass! I take a further gander of the room I'm in, OH MY GOD! I AM ON DANCING WITH THE STARS!!!! WITH ALL THE MEN I THINK ARE HOT IN THIS WORLD! Why are there no female stars? (Oh yeah, maybe because this is MY daydream! Ha!) I hear the audience go crazy as Trent and his partner start doing the tango. Wow, Trent Reznor doing the tango. I look up on the monitor, he's so graceful. Never moved like that at any of the concerts I've seen him at. And that toe point. Wow!

I see Alan Rickman in the corner going over his dance with his partner. I chuckle out loud at how funny Alan looks doing the running man. Then it hits me, who's my partner!!!?? I start scanning the room to find my hot male dancer partner. I see Chino Moreno, no he's with someone. I see Johnny Depp, oh that's original. He's dressed as a pirate. Suddenly I feel arms around my waist from behind and hot breath at my neck. A deep voice whispers in my ear, "Ready to do this hot stuff?" I turn around...

Me: "JOHN! What are you doing here? You're not a star!!!"

John: "Ahhh but you are."He kisses me on the cheek and I close my eyes for a second.

John: "Honey?"

I open my eyes. I'm in my bedroom.

John: "Daydreaming again? Hmm?" He laughs. "Come on doll face, we're going to be late for the concert if we don't leave right now!"

We are going to this totally great 80's music night at the Greek Theatre. Human League. B-52's. It's going to be a blast! The Greek over the Hollywood Bowl any day! <3 the Greek. Maybe Alan Rickman will be there. Have a beautiful night!

Tian

Today has been a lovely day. Slightly foggy. Cool enough for a sweater. I have water boiling for fresh tea. There have been several people in the shop today. At the moment, there is a gentleman wandering around. He looks a bit hopeless. I think I will offer him some tea, and a seat on this love seat passed down from my grandmother Qing. My grandmother's name means "clarity". My grandmother could always see into the souls of people. See what pained them and offer solutions. My grandmother was a treasure among humans. I welcome the lost man and gave him a steaming cup of tea.

Tian: "Please, won't you have a look around? There may be something to your liking."

THE END

28946481R00170

Made in the USA
San Bernardino, CA
10 January 2016